GLIMPSES OF TRUTH

"Janie felt her Grandfather at her side and the photographer, noting her expression, quickly snapped her picture."

GLIMPSES OF TRUTH

by

EDITH JANE HANDS

Dragonfire Books
20 South Hill Park
London NW3 2SB

Published by Dragonfire Books,
20 South Hill Park, London NW3 2SB
Cover illustration by Heidi Ferid

ISBN 0 9513606 0 4

Printed in Great Britain by A. Wheaton & Co Ltd,
Hennock Road, Marsh Barton,
Exeter

CONTENTS.

Chapter 1: Janie and Grandad. Page 1

Chapter 2: Disaster at the Button Factory. Page 7

Chapter 3: Growing Up. Page 11

Chapter 4: Dancing at "Birds". Page 15

Chapter 5: The Coffee Stained Dress. Page 19

Chapter 6: The Tall Dark Stranger. Page 25

Chapter 7: Sunday Tea Ceremony. Page 31

Chapter 8: Making a Match of It. Page 33

Chapter 9: Early Married Life. Page 37

Chapter 10: Astral Adventure. Page 41

Chapter 11: A Pathway to Truth. Page 47

Chapter 12: 'Going to Church.' Page 55

Chapter 13: The Rose in the Coffin. Page 59

Chapter 14: The Home Circle. Page 63

Chapter 15: Glimpses of Truth. Page 69

Chapter 16: The Model Railway. Page 73

Chapter 17: Janie's Greatest Proof. Page 77

Chapter 18: A Cavalier Bodyguard. Page 83

Chapter 19: The Dark Days Begin. Page 87

Chapter 20: Escape to the Country. Page 91

Chapter 21: The Nursery Bedroom. Page 97

Chapter 22: A House of Their Own. Page 101

Chapter 23: New and Broken Circles. Page 109

Chapter 24: The Sanctuary at 'Pinewoods.' Page 115

Chapter 25: Earthly and Spiritual Surgery. Page 119

Chapter 26: An Amazing Operation. Page 127

Chapter 27: A Wonderful Gift. Page 133

Chapter 28: 'A Snip, a Twist, and a Stitch.' Page 135

Chapter 29: The Spirit World Nursery. Page 139

Chapter 30: The Parting of the Ways. Page 145

FOREWORD.

Open my eyes that I may see
Glimpses of truth Thou hast for me.
Help me to set the higher self free
So shall I serve and worship Thee.

from a Spiritualist hymn.

When I started this book I did not intend it to be an autobiography of my life. Because of family commitments I decided to write it in story form. Most of the names are fictitious but all the spiritual experiences that I have quoted are absolutely true.

The "Janie" in the story is really myself, Edith Jane Hands.

CHAPTER 1:

JANIE AND GRANDAD.

Janie ran down the entry, a passageway between the houses, out on to the darkening street, and stood gazing out across the chimneypots, towards the setting sun dying redly in the twilight sky. A slight sob filled her throat and a great yearning came over her to stretch out her arms and fly away to the rosy land beyond the sunset.

Every evening whenever she could, she went through this same ritual; why she did so she could never say. Twilight always made her feel sad and depressed, as though she was an exile far from home. Somehow, she felt she belonged to the golden land behind the sun.

As the light faded, she shivered in the chill air, and turning retraced her footsteps up the dark entry to the house on the right. Her mother met her on the doorstep; "I was just coming to look for you," she said, "how many times have I told you not to run out without a coat, it's chilly tonight as well. Do you want that bad cough back again, tearing at y'chest? Anyway, where have y'been?"

The two walked into the kitchen, and Janie, hearing sounds which told her that her two sisters were in the "front room", turned to her mother. "I went into the street to see the sunset." Then, meeting her mother's puzzled gaze, she asked, "Mom, do you think there is a golden land behind the sunset?" "Janie, where on earth do you get such ideas from? Is it the books you get from that library? I said you were too young to join, filling y'head with such things."

Janie's face turned red as she protested. "But I ain't young Mom. It's my birthday next month and I start my teens and this time next year I'll be going to work. Besides, it wasn't the books;" she took a deep breath and lowered her voice as she imparted a profound fact. "Grandad told me." "He did?" Mrs. Pullen sat down suddenly, as though she could not take in such a confession standing up. "What else has he told you, to mither y'head with?" Janie sank down on the rug besides her mother, her blue-green eyes bright with memory, and her young voice quick and eager. "Grandad said, someday we all will go to the land behind the sun – he called it the land of dreams, where all our wishes came true, that is, if we have led a good life and remembered the things Jesus taught. He also told me about the stars – that someday, someone will make a balloon to take men to them and they will find people living on them."

Janie paused for breath while her mother stared at her open-mouthed; then with a tender expression, she stooped to kiss her daughter on her forehead. "Come, child, it's bedtime; call Jessie and Julie, get washed and up that wooden hill with you."

Jane Pullen's daughters were triplets. Jessie and Julie were alike as two peas, small and petite, with dark brown hair and eyes to match. Janie was tall and slender, her fair clear skin matching the pale gold of her hair. As the doctor who brought them into the world had said, "No doubt about it, the two small ones are identical twins, but where t'other one came in, God only knows."

Janie, being the eldest of the three, (by at least twenty minutes), was called on to help with the various chores about the house, and because, with her long legs, she went like the wind to run any errands that were needed, both for her mother and the neighbours, who paid her accordingly. She was always pleased to earn a few coppers, as money was very scarce in the Pullen household. Dad was working now, but his job was poorly paid, so Mom went working as a "char" for sixpence an hour.

Just recently, Mom had required Janie to visit her grandfather at weekends to help in the house and run the necessary errands. Grandmother had fallen off a chair while reaching up to a cupboard and hurt her back, so housework had become a burden for her.

They lived about two miles from the Pullen home, but Jane sped through the streets after leaving school on Friday afternoon, clutching the brown paper parcel, containing her nightdress and hairbrush and comb, toothbrush and two clean handcherchiefs. She could not reach her destination quick enough; a whole weekend with Grandad was a wonderful prospect, while Monday morning, when she went to school, seemed far away.

She worshipped her grandfather, with his gentle kindly ways, deep searching eyes and short neatly trimmed beard. Besides, there was something in his expression which told her Mom belonged to him, and she loved her mother dearly. Also, Grandad was so clever. He had many stories to tell of when he was a younger man and had travelled to so many places, and his explanation of the stars, with their grand sounding names, filled her with wonder. And who else but Grandad could tell her of that land beyond the golden road that stretched from the rosy sunset? He told her he had only gone there in his dreams, but one day he would go to stay, and he would find a way to help her to stay awhile with him in her dreams.

It was all a puzzle to Janie, but she was only too willing to leave everything in the capable hands of that beloved old man. The weekend passed much the same as the other days spent with her grandparents. She swept, scrubbed and dusted, until the house shone like a new pin. The shopping was done in the company of her grandad, then, on Sunday morning, while her grandmother prepared the dinner, she donned the pretty pink dress that Mom had made, and the cream straw hat with it's pink ribbon, and, taking the old man's hand, tripped happily along on that sober Sunday morning walk.

But somehow, Grandad did not seem his old talkative self, for when they walked in the park he sat down more often on the benches that lined the path. He pressed her hand firmly, while now and again he stared down at her with rather troubled eyes. "Are you tired, Grandad?" the child asked, remembering that Mom had told her she must not let Grandad walk too far without resting. "Yes, little one, I think perhaps I am." He closed his eyes a moment and stifled a sigh, then, feeling the anxiety from the girl at his side, he roused himself to put an arm around her shoulders.

"Little one," he said, "Do you remember what I told you about the land beyond the sunset?" "Yes, Grandad."

The old man studied the young face, serious with dawning apprehension. "Perhaps, in a little while, I may be called away; but remember, Janie, I will never forget you, I will always try to be near you. Think of me sometimes. I know, as the years go by, and you live your life, as you must, the memory of me will die, but try never to forget the things we have talked about. Keep Christ's teachings in your heart and use them as a pattern for your way of life. Enjoy yourself, little one; God did not mean us always to be serious – He gave us the gift of laughter as well as the gift of tears. And in the years to come, when you have found your path in life, you will come to know more of that golden land."

The child buried her face against the old man's shoulder, while a sob quivered through her frame. "But I don't want you to go away, Grandad; how can you be near me and yet be away from me? If you must go, please take me with you."

"No, no, my child, that cannot be. But come, let us not be sad on this lovely morning. See, I am rested now. Let us make our way slowly home, and see what joy awaits us from the efforts of your nanny's cooking." He drew Janie gently to him and tenderly kissed the tear-stained face. But now the sun had ceased to shine for her, and she clung tightly to her Grandad's hand as they made their way home in silence. Something in his manner forbade her pursuing their talk further.

Monday morning came all too quickly and she felt very sad as she prepared herself for school. She at last kissed her grandmother goodbye and listened attentively to her last minute instructions. Her grandfather walked with her to the street, where he gathered her gently in his arms.

"Farewell, little one," he whispered, "Try not to worry; you must not be sad, it's just a phase in life that must be faced. May God give you courage and comfort." So saying, he kissed her warmly. Janie clung to him and, after returning his caress, broke away from him and sped lightly down the street.

The days went on as usual for Janie, but she went around with a heavy heart. Somehow she could not bring herself to tell even her mother of her grandfather's intended departure; perhaps, after all, he might not have to go and it was usless causing Mom unnecessary worry.

She awoke on Friday morning with the prospect of the coming weekend on her mind. She jumped out of bed and prepared to dress, when the door burst open and Jessie ran into the room, her eyes wide with a mixture of alarm and excitement. "Janie, Mom's crying, I think something has happened to Grandad."

Janie stiffened with foreboding, then, without speaking, she pushed her sister aside and ran down the narrow staircase. Sure enough, Mom sat weeping, the corner of her white apron thrown over her face, while Dad stood awkwardly at the gas stove making a pot of tea.

"Mom, please what is wrong, what has happened to Grandad?"

Janie knelt in front of her mother and in her anxiety pulled the apron from her face. Her mother stared with red swollen eyes at the white young face in front of her and her sobs broke out afresh.

Mr. Pullen turned from the stove, his face stern with unaccustomed emotion. "Janie," he said, his voice betraying his concern, "Young Jim Lightfoot has just brung us some bad news; y'grandfather was took bad and – he's died."

A cry of anguish rang through the kitchen. "No, oh no, not that; Grandad said he may have to go away, but not to die – oh Dad, Dad, what shall I do?" The young voice trailed away in a flood of broken sobs. By this time Jessie and Julie had entered the kitchen; both stood in awed silence, clasping each other tightly as if giving each moral support.

"Janie, Janie, don't take on so – these things happen; he was an old man, it's better that way." But Janie heeded not her father's plea; her heart was broken, she felt that the end of the world had come. Never again would she walk with her grandfather, her hand clasped in his; never again would she listen to his kind gentle voice, imparting words of wisdom and stories of wonder and mystery.

And so the hours dragged by. Mom dried her eyes and busied herself with the funeral preparations. She decided that the triplets should attend the service to be held in the little church within the cemetery gates. Black dresses would have to be provided, but money was scarce; therefore, the pretty pink dresses were sacrificed, and looked hideous after Mom had dipped them in black dye. The pink ribbon on the cream straw hats was replaced by black. The sisters stared blankly at the dismal array; then Jessie and Julie burst into tears, while Janie protested hotly that Grandad would never have agreed to the change. He loved the pink dresses, and what did a funeral matter anyway? Mom was slightly shocked as she looked at her offspring disapprovingly; then, declaring that black was the colour for funerals and only in that colour could you respectfully follow the dead to their last resting place, she told them not to be so silly and to behave themselves.

The day arrived and the triplets slowly followed the black procession into the little cemetery church. In the pew Janie knelt between her two sisters – and although her heart was sad, her eyes were dry. There was a strangeness about her; she felt somehow she must wait patiently and watch. The drone of the minister's voice and the perfume from the flowers of the nearby wreaths, made her feel relaxed and at peace, and it was with reluctance that she rose to her feet as the organ played the opening lines of the psalm, "Yes, though I walk through death's dark vale....."

She dreamily surveyed the long flower-decked coffin resting in front of the plain little altar and her mind could not accept that her dear, dear Grandad could possibly be imprisoned therein. She looked up towards the stream of sunlight, forcing itds way through the deep blue and red of the coloured window, and all at once, through the rainbow haze she saw the head and shoulders of her beloved grandparent. Her heart pounded joyously.

"Grandad, oh, grandad," she breathed, "I know you did not die." The penetrating eyes sought her out among the pews, and, smiling reassuringly, the vision slowly faded.

CHAPTER 2:

DISASTER AT THE BUTTON FACTORY.

So life went on, rather monotonously, for the triplets. At fourteen they finished with school life and went to work at the local "sewing factory", a huge concern which employed hundreds of women and girls, all working in the varied processes of turning out ladies' and childrens' wear. Janie was eventually installed in the embroidery department, and she grew to love her work with it's every-changing patterns and variety of coloured silks.

Jessie, in the packing department, settled down with a sober determination to be good at her job, but poor Janie made various changes in the first two years of her working life, and at last left the sewing factory, after finding herself a job in an erinite button factory. This arrangement caused Mom a certain amount of anxiety, as the factory was a good distance from home, which meant that Julie could not get home for the mid-day dinner break, and what would she do after she had eaten her sandwiches? Mom's mind ran amok, she could not bear the thought of any harm coming to her girls. There was no doubt about it, Janie must give up her embroidery and go to work with her sister.

Janie protested hotly, for her job had turned out well and she managed to earn a good wage on the piecework basis employed at the factory. But Mom was firm in her decision, so Janie was duly installed in her new job as a sort of general help around the small office and factory. The work was varied and interesting and Janie appreciated the responsibility placed on her. She was also able to keep a watchful eye on Julie, who appeared to have settled down and liked her job of cutting the erinite into long narrow strips on a small machine.

Besides, the girls loved the walk to work each morning; they could have gone by tram, but the jolting and stopping and starting caused Janie to feel terribly sick, so she used the trams as little as possible, and the coins saved were certainly an advantage. After leaving the long streets behind, the way led into the countryside, and they walked between fields of wild flowers and fresh spring grass. The journey was not lonely, as other pedestrians, cyclists and an occasional motor-car used the long country road, which led into the neighbouring suburb, with its rows of genteel houses, a few necessary shops, and a scattering of small factories.

The few girls and women with whom the sisters worked were on the whole jolly and friendly; one girl in particular, Mary Harper, took the girls under her wing and helped them through the day. During the midday break, if the weather was fine, the three would hurry to a nearby park, to sit in the green splendour to eat their sandwiches and drink the hot tea from the thermos flask.

They chattered as only three girls together can chatter, before returning to their work, both physically and mentally refreshed. Mary Harper had many stories to tell of her family – mother, father, three brothers and an older sister named Vera, who was engaged to be married to a young electrician, John Bailey. According to Mary, who adored John, he was much too good for her selfish sister. He earned good money by working long hours overtime and spent a great deal of it on presents for his ungrateful fiancee, who took everything for granted and could scarcely say "thank you." She was rarely in a good mood and picked a quarrel at the slightest provocation.

Janie secretly thought it a strange situation, and decided that John Bailey needed a good shaking for putting up with such a surly fiancee; it was certainly not a good basis for a happy marriage. So life went on for Janie and Julie, while Jessie, safe and secure in the packing department of the sewing factory, missed her sisters very much and wished they could be working together under the one roof. Janie had no doubt she could have got work at the button factory, but Jessie was not at all venturesome, and decided to keep the security of her "little rut."

In all this time Janie often thought of the man who had coloured her childhood and had made life so exciting for her. The ache in her heart was still there when she remembered the kindly eyes, the gentle voice and the tender clasp of his hands. The memory of the sweet vision in the little church still filled her with wonder, and during the times it nestled in her mind, her grandfather was very close to her. Also, there were the dreams – what had he told her? "One day I will go to stay in the land of dreams and I will find a way of helping you to stay a while with me." From time to time she met him in a beautiful garden and they walked hand in hand together, talking, laughing, and oh, so happy. And when she woke, she could remember the garden and the glorious flowers that grew in profusion, and the touch of his hand was still with her. She could remember the light swinging step from a body that had become young again. She could still hear his voice, sometimes gay, often earnest, his words eluding her, though she felt they were profound.

*   *   *

It had been a busy day for Janie, packing the white boxes of carded buttons into the large wooden crates, ready for when the railwaymen called to take them to the station, en route for delivery. She looked at the clock and noted it was time to take the delivery invoices across to the office to be signed. The office was apart from the factory, across a small yard which was also shared by two men who ran a motor repair business.

Janie opened the door leading into the yard and stood hesitating on the step. For no apparent reason she felt reluctant to proceed further. Looking across the yard she noticed two men doing something to a huge gasometer which stood a short distance from the office door. As she stared, a voice, curt and clear, which seemed to be inside her head, commanded: "Do not cross the yard! Go back inside!"

Puzzled and a little frightened, Janie slowly returned to her work table. Glancing at the crates she realised the men would soon arrive for them, and the invoices must be signed. Deliberating, she gazed around the room, wishing that Mr. Mills, 'the Boss', would come in; he could sign the papers, then there would be no need for her to go to the office. Suddenly, there was a dreadful explosion, which lifted Janie clean off her stool, throwing her against the crates; she lay there, clutching her head in pain and fright. Pandemonium broke loose. The roof had caved in, debris was falling everywhere, while screaming women ran blindly through the fog and dust, searching for the exits.

Janie scrambled to her feet, feeling sick and shaken, with a strong urge to get out into the cool, fresh air. Her head swimming she looked about her, and saw, to her dismay, that several crates had fallen in an untidy mass around her, blocking her exit. She tried to push one, but it was impossible to move it, while each time she made to climb, she slithered down, grazing her shins against the rough wood.

The screams of the women had faded away, and Janie felt isolated in the fog of still falling rubbish. Several times she called out, but her cries went unheeded. Then murmuring, "Please, God, help me!" she was aware that she was falling, falling – into a dark space.

Voices penetrated her consciousness, and a cold breeze caressed her aching brow. An anxious voice was saying, "But I'm sure, Mr. Mills, I saw Janie sitting at her table, seconds before the bang – I know I did, sir." "All right, Mary! Then where is she? I know I saw her making for the office, about five seconds before the explosion; she must have – oh, my goodness! Those crates......"

The voice trailed off; a rush of footsteps as Mr. Mills entered the building, and Janie struggled to her feet, not quite knowing where she was. "Jane, Jane Pullen! Where are you?" the worried man called, and promptly collided with the shaken girl. He helped her outside, and as Janie glanced at the strained faces of her fellow workers, she suddenly remembered her sister.

"Julie! Julie! I must go back to look for her – ."

"Janie, I'm here – I'm all right! But you! Are you hurt? You look so strange," and Julie, trembling and worried, hurried forward to help support her sister.

By this time, firemen and policemen were on the scene, while residents from the neighbouring houses took the women and girls into their homes to fortify them with hot sweet tea. A kindly woman made Janie comfortable in a large easy chair, and, telling Julie and Mary Harper to keep an eye on her, bustled out into the kitchen to make the tea. After a while, Mr. Mills came in to see how the girls were, and seeing Janie appeared much better, with the colour back in her cheeks, told them that the cause of the explosion came from the gasometer, and that the two men who had been working on it had been killed instantly.

Janie shuddered as she realised she was possibly the last person to see them alive, and also, if it had not been for 'the voice', she would have ended her life with them. She looked up and saw Mr. Mills watching her curiously. "Tell me, Jane," he said, "why did you change your mind about going back to the office? I saw you going in that direction, but you must have turned back or you would have...have...." His voice trailed off in an embarrassed silence as he stared awkwardly at the three girls.

"You mean – if I got to those two men I would have died with them!" Janie's voice faltered as she recalled the warning order; a voice in her hed, belonging to someone she could not see – they would all think her mad; and yet it had saved her life. And who had rescued her from behind those awful crates? "It was a voice, Mr. Mills," she declared, "when I got to the yard I just could not walk across to the office, something seemed to hold me back; then I heard a voice telling me to go back inside, not to cross the yard." "A voice! But where did it come from? Whose voice do you mean? Why, it must have known there was going to be an explosion, who was it? We must clear this up ......" He stopped as he noticed the bewildered expression on Janie's expressive face and his own showed deep concern as the girl answered: "It did not belong to anyone, at least not that I could see; it seemed to be inside my head and it was quite loud and clear, it's stupid, I know, but it did save my life."
remember what really did happen. Here is some money for your tram fare, and just take care." The girls thanked him and the woman whose house they were in, then made their way home, for once silent, each girl occupied with her own thoughts.

Mom was horrified as her girls narrated the events of the afternoon; to think, she might never have seen them alive again. She even forgot to scold Janie when she was told about the "voice" and the mysterious rescue from the jumble of crates. Or perhaps, Mom was wise in the matter of voices and unseen help; she was not her father's daughter for nothing.

The girls never went back to Mr. Mills' button factory. Once was enough for Mom. Dad suggested that Janie should again apply for her embroidery job at the dress factory, and Julie could seek a situation in a large printing works that "a chap at our shop" had told him about.

CHAPTER 3:

GROWING UP.

So, in due course, Janie and Julie were settled in earning their livelihood – Janie working at her beloved embroidery, while Julie tussled with the workings of a multigraph machine at the printing works, a job she found interesting and rewarding, as her wages proved to be somewhat higher than either Janie's or Jessie's.

The triplets were members of the parish church, situated at the top of the street in which they lived. Two or three evenings a week, after their evening meal, they made their way to the church hall, to take part in the various social functions held there. Monday evening was "drama group", in which the young people of the Sunday School took part. This was Janie's favourite; she usually had a part in the various plays, as she had a flair for comedy and a fine voice for singing in the operettas. There was always such a lot to do, what with rehearsals, costumes to be made and sorted out and "sets" to be designed. The young people thoroughly enjoyed themselves, their good-natured fun and laughter ringing through the hall.

On Saturday evenings, a dance would be held in the hall, with Mr. Grant, the choir master, playing the current 'dance tunes' on the 'grand piano'. The girls could scarcely contain themselves until the 'great evening' arrived. Mom had made them each a pretty dance dress, for their sixteenth birthdays, all the same pattern – a bodice of silky material, with short puffed sleeves and a full lace skirt – but Julie and Jessie chose a light blue colour, while Janie decided on lavender, which went so well with her extreme fairness.

All the girls, of various ages, thronged into the dressing-room, which led off the main hall, to hang up their outdoor clothes and change into their satin dance shoes, with the rather high heels. Then out came the combs and facepowder, in some cases lipstick, and the girls would proceed to make the most of their charms. The triplets wore their hair in the 'bobbed style', which was the fashion then; some of the older girls had their hair 'marcel waved', for this grand occasion, but Janie was fortunate in having natural wavy hair, while her sisters, although not wavy, could always manage to comb their hair in a most becoming way which suited them admirably. Mom didn't mind her girls using a minimum of face powder, but lipstick was out of the question – only "low factory girls" found it necessary to use that commodity, and Mom was determined to keep her daughters on a higher respectable level. So Janie and her sisters carefully powdered their faces, then bit and rubbed their lips to draw the red blood into them. After peering critically in the large mirror, they joined their own special friends and made their way into the dance hall. Most of the young men were congregated together, talking and laughing in groups, but, as the girls made their entry, a silence fell, as they surveyed the colourful array.

Mr. Grant, noting that the young people were assembled, struck up the opening waltz. The girls, seated on the chairs, appeared indifferent to the presence of their male counterparts, but a pounding of hearts and a rise of colour to the cheeks, made it obvious that they had noticed their favourite partner was making his way towards them. Soon, the dancing was in full progress and the happiness and gaiety of the young people were complete.

Although the triplets did most things together, Jessie and Julie, being identical twins, liked to pair off together, leaving Janie alone.

So, consequently, she struck up a friendship with Nora James, a ginger-haired girl, about her own age. The four girls went to Sunday School and church together on Sundays, while after mid-day dinner they made their way to the nearby park. It seemed that on sunny Sundays throughout the year, all the youth for miles around flocked to the beautiful grounds with the acres of well-kept lawns, colourful flower-beds; the two large ponds, with the ornamental fountains, where boats could be hired for a few coppers for the hour. In the centre of the largest green, stood a bandstand, and on Sundays and holidays, a brass band poured out its bright and gay music.

Janie loved the happy, colourful scene, with the lads and lassies passing each other on the stony paths, the while they exchanged coquettish glances, and sometimes stopped to laugh and chatter; the excited cries and calls of the children playing around, while Moms and Dads sat on the wooden benches and talked, as they kept a watchful eye on their offspring. It was the joyful day of the monotonous week, for most of these people worked long hours in stuffy factories to earn enough to keep body and soul together.

The early twenties saw the start of a struggle to better the lot of the working man. Woman, too, was viewing the horizon where she could tgake a more active part in the running of a prosperous country. But the struggle was hard and slow, and the middle-aged folk were tired and discouraged after going through the nightmare of a world at war. The young appreciated what must be done to better their lives, but the lean years of the war and immediately afterwards, which brought self-denial and lack of social activities, made them determined to seek pleasures and have a good time, while they were young enough to enjoy them.

Dance-halls sprang up in every district and cinemas and theatres opened their doors to packed audiences. Outdoor sports were coming into their own; on every hand, man was determined to seek a warm glow to his otherwise gray existence.

So, this was the world into which the triplets were born. Their instinct was to follow the crowd and to accept with both hands what pleasures the world had to offer. Their capacity to enjoy life was greater than the pitfalls that might await them. They loved to sing and to listen to good music, while in their gayer moods dancing and laughter at good clean fun, coloured their leisure hours.

Jane and Bert Pullen realised their daughters' world was vastly different to the world they had known in their youth. The stuffiness and narrow-mindedness of the Victorian era had been swept away in the changes the war had brought. Nevertheless, three daughters of the same age were a great responsibility, so Dad decided that a little of the Victorian strictness would not harm them – would indeed keep them on the narrow path of respectability that meant so much to the honest poor of that time.

They could go out two or three evenings a week, provided they attended church activities, and were home by ten o'clock. They could also go the Institute dance which was held once a month on a Saturday evening and was over by 10.30 pm. The evenings they stayed at home were spent in helping Mom around the house. There was always the inevitable pile of washing to be ironed – Mom 'took in' the washing of a doctor's family who lived near the park, and also that of a widower who lived alone – brasses to be cleaned, and the parlour furniture to be polished.

Janie still kept up her membership of the local library. She would read every spare moment she could find. She had long graduated from Sir Rider Haggard's books, with their wonderful travel and adventure stories, together with the tales of the culture and mysticism of a lost ancient race, to stories of the family life of that fortunate section of society called "the better class". Now, she was wading through a book on Theosophy, but was finding it rather 'hard going'. Perhaps, seventeen was too early to 'stand and stare', and to wonder what purpose in life God had in store for one. If Grandad were here, he would soon explain the mystery in the pages; she felt, somehow, that the things he used to talk about were connected. she sighed as she wished she could be with him again, if only for a short while.

And so the days passed swiftly as the sisters worked hard and enjoyed their leisure hours, while they went on with the serious business of 'growing up'. As their nineteenth birthday approached, Janie spent more of her time with Nora James. The two girls got on well together; apart from dancing, they would take long walks through the richer parts of the town and view with interest the large well-kept houses. Janie loved the signs of affluence – the expensive curtains at the windows, the lawns and lovely flower-beds of the front gardens.

Although she never hoped herself to live in such surroundings, she was glad that there were people who could make them possible – to walk through the quiet, clean roads with the beautiful houses on either side brought a peace and warm glow to her artistic soul. On the other hand, the slums and signs of poverty made her sad and depressed. Janie's family and friends lived in between the two – although poor and money was not plentiful, their small houses were kept clean and bright and the 'handcherchief gardens' neat and tidy.

CHAPTER 4:

DANCING AT 'BIRDS'.

October lst, 1927 – Janie opened her eyes on that rather chilly morning and realised that it was somehow a special day. Memory returned; "Of course!" she remembered, as she sprang out of bed, "it's our birthday! I wonder if the postman has been." She quickly dressed and, going out on to the landing, knocked at her sisters' door. "Hurry up, you two," she called, "do you know what day it is?" Sleepy grumbles answered her; then, as Mom's voice sounded at the foot of the stairs, "Postman's been," two excited girls were heard tumbling out of bed.

And so the sisters had reached the final year of their teens. Mom was very proud of her girls although she wouldn't dream of imparting the fact. Dad, on the other hand, loved people to know how he regarded his rather special offspring. Every year, on the anniversary of their birth, usually on the Sunday afternoon nearest to that day, he would have Mom dress the triplets in their best attire, then would marshall them through the streets to a small family photographer to have their pictures taken.

Their nineteenth birthday was no exception; but Dad was in for a surprise. The girls did not want to be taken together, they wanted their own photograph. He argued; the girls protested. Then, staring at them open-mouthed, he realised they were fast 'growing up'. He quietly gave in.

Secretly, for some time, Janie had been saving a few pence each week in a 'photographic club', run by a girl at work. The studio was in a high-class part of a main road leading to the city. The evening before her appointment, Janie stayed at home to shampoo her blonde hair.

Next day, Janie felt like a princess as she donned her best attire and set off alone to the photographer's studio. She felt rather nervous as she was ushered into the 'camera' room to face a rather tired-looking middle-aged man. However, his face brightened as he appraisingly looked her over. "Head and shoulders or full length?" he inquired, as he adjusted the camera. "Pardon? Oh – er – you mean, what type of picture," Janie stammered, "Oh, head and shoulders, please, and I don't want to grin, I want to look my age." "And what may that be?" the man asked, smiling. "Nineteen, aye! Just on the threshold of womanhood – well, we must have you looking a bit dignified, mustn't we? But it's up to you – think of something that makes you happy, we don't want you looking too serious."

For no apparent reason, Janie suddenly felt her Grandfather at her side, her hand clasped in his, and the photographer, noting her expression, quickly 'snapped' the picture.

Two weeks to wait for the result. Janie walked soberly home; somehow she felt a change in herself – that important happenings were looming on her horizon.

*   *   *

The evening of the same day, the sisters, all dressed up for the occasion, attended a special meal at the Church Hall. Nora James was also there and the girls enjoyed their usual happy time. During the interval, while the pianist rested from his labours and everyone partook of light refreshments, Nora drew Janie aside to an isolated corner, whispering that she had something to tell her. "Next Saturday, I'm going to Bird's," she imparted, in an excited whisper, "will you come with me?"

Janie stared at her friend wide-eyed, unable to speak. "Well," said Nora, impatiently, "what do you say? Will you come with me?" Janie came out of her trance; "Did you say 'Bird's?'" "Yes, I did," Nora stated, a trifle arrogantly; "I suppose your Mother won't let you go."

"But, it isn't a nice place; Mom says well-brought up girls don't want to go to places like Bird's," Janie stammered.

"What does your Mother know about it? She's never been. A girl I work with went there last Saturday and she says it's wonderful; it's a lovely room and a six-piece band, with a Master of Ceremonies and a gorgeous floor – and things are run properly, and – and everything's above board." Nora paused for breath, as she closely watched Janie's face for the effect of her words.

Janie felt uncomfortable, because she was tempted; but she also knew her Mother would never approve. To her, regular dance-halls were not decent or suitable for young girls to spend their leisure hours in. There was not the supervision of the Church Hall, and Mom imagined all sorts of wrong things happening there. But Janie thought Bird's might be different. After all, it was a small select dancing school, which taught pupils during the week, then opened its doors on Saturday, so that that the general public might witness how well the would-be dancers were taught.

For a few moments the two girls stared at each othr, then Nora, noting her friend's indecision, tossed her head angrily. "All right," she snapped, "I'll find someone else to go with; no-one would think you were nineteen – you daren't do this and you daren't do the other. It's about time you and your Mother realised you are now grown up."

"All right – all right, Nora, there's no need to get nasty; I'll think about it, I'll let you know before we go home."

But the rest of the evening was spoiled for Janie. She knew her Mother would never give her permission. On the other hand, her curiosity was aroused; she would like to see what sort of place Bird's was, and surely going just one week would not hurt; what Mom did not know about, she could not grieve over. The more she thought it over, the more exciting it seemed, until at the end of the eveing she told her friend she would go with her.

The next Saturday happened to be the Institute evening, and Bird's was situated in a quiet little street almost opposite, so it was quite convenient for the two girls to run across the road from the Institute and the few yards down the side road to the forbidden establishment. Of course, Jessie and Julie had to be told the secret; the disapproval in their brown eyes made Janie uncomfortable – she could see her Mother looking at her.

"You can come with us, if you like," she stammered; but Jessie shook her head and started up the steps of the Institute, pulling Julie along with her. "No, thanks!" she called, "our partners are here; and if anything happens, don't forget, it's nothing to do with us."

"Don't be daft, what can happen, it's only a dancing school." Janie suddenly felt very cross, as the angry tears started to her eyes. Anybody would think she was a little girl – after all she was nineteen.

She turned to Nora who stood grinning at her side. "Oh, come on, let's go, it's all so silly; I wish I had told Mom, now," she said, defiantly, "after all, it was some time ago that she forbade us to go to the regular dance-halls, we are much older now."

The girls entered the rather dull-looking building, but once inside the vestibule, Janie gazed approvingly around her. A thick blue carpet covered the floor, while a soft amber light glowed from a glass chandelier. All around the walls were flowering potted plants; a pleasant fragrant perfume caressed Janie's nostrils as she advanced rather shyly to the small ticket office. Nora asked for two tickets and also to be directed to the ladies' cloakroom. "Through the glass doors, ladies' cloakroom on the right, men on the left, dance room through the swing doors at the end."

Janie felt a thrill of excitement as she changed into her black satin dance shoes; everything seemed so nice, even the middle-aged woman attendant, who was busy putting away their coats on hangers, had assured them that they would have a lovely time. She joined Nora at the large mirror hanging on one wall and after combing their hair and lightly powdering their faces, both girls stood back to survey their reflections. Nora sighed as she surveyed Janie's results. "Oh, Jane," she uttered enviously, "I do wish my hair was like yours – all wavy and fluffy – mine's as straight as a poker and so inclined to be greasy. I'm going to save up and have one of those perms, I know they're dear, but it will be worth it." "Never mind, Nora," Janie sympathised, "your hair's a lovely colour, so it doesn't matter about it being straight, and your green dress does suit you well." Nevertheless, she felt pleased and satisfied as she noted how attractive she looked in her new mauve dress so suited to her tall slim figure.

The two girls entered the dance-room and, although she did not realise it, Janie had reached a very important milestone in her young life.

CHAPTER 5:

THE COFFEE-STAINED DRESS.

A colourful, bright and happy scene met their eager gaze. It was a lovely room, decorated tastefully in white and gold. On a dais at one end, the members of a six-piece band were busy tuning their instruments and sorting over sheets of music.

All around the highly polished floor were rows of chairs for the convenience of the dancers, and Janie, noting two vacant ones halfway down the room, made her way to them through the small groups of girls and young men who stood around, Nora close on her heels.

"Well!" exclaimed that young lady, as they seated themselves, "what do you think of it, eh? Isn't it posh?"

"Oh! it's wonderful, Nora; I'm so glad we came. Oh, look! there's some girls from work – I didn't know they came here." Janie started to her feet to wave excitedly to a group of girls who stood talking together across the floor. One of them looked up and noticed the waving arm; then, recognising the face and form that went with it, she said something to her companions and all four tripped across to join the two girls.

They expressed their surprise at seeing Janie there, but assured her and Nora that they would have the time of their lives. Ada, the eldest of the girls, looked approvingly at Janie; she noticed the sparkle in the blue-green eyes, the softly curled blonde hair, framing a face not beautifully but unusually attractive, the smiling lips revealing white even teeth.

"You look very nice, Jane," she said, "your dress suits you perfectly." "Oh, thank you, Ada, Mom would be pleased, she made it for me," and inside Janie flushed with pleasure at the unexpected compliment, which added greatly to her charm.

The band struck up the first foxtrot, and the four girls made off towards a corner of the room where stood a medley of male would-be dancers, promising Janie and Nora that they would look them up later on. The two friends got to their feet, anxious to join in the foxtrot, as they knew that they would not invite a male partner, unless they could show they were experienced dancers. The next dance was a waltz and as the dreamy music floated around the room, Janie and Nora sat expectantly, wondering if they would draw a partner. Then Janie, not liking to stare deliberately across the room to the groups of male dancers standing around, focussed her attention on the orchestra, when Nora suddenly dug her in the ribs with her elbow.

"Look!" she whispered excitedly, "there's two fellows coming for us, I'm sure; they are staring at us."

Janie looked in the direction indicated, and saw two young men walking in their direction. One was tall, quite six foot, and dark; the other above medium height, light-brown hair and a fair complexion. Both were very well dressed in navy blue suits and white shirts, a fact which aroused Janie's approval – she could not stand slovenly-dressed boys. "Boys?" she thought, puckering her brow, while she just had time to whisper, "They're a bit old."

The smaller of the two looked down at Janie and with a friendly smile said, "Will you please have this dance with me?"

"Certainly," smiled Janie, getting to her feet, and as they waltzed off in line with the dancers, she noticed that Nora had paired off with his tall friend.

That was a wonderful dance. Janie loved every minute of it. Their steps harmonised perfectly, over the polished floor, while the rhythm from the music of the lovely 'Vienna Waltz' gave them that first-class timing that is so essential to good dancing. The music stopped, but the dancers remained on the floor and clapped enthusiastically for an encore.

As Janie and her partner glided off again, he looked down at her and remarked, inquiring, "You are a good dancer! I haven't seen you before; is this your first time?"

"Oh yes! I have been dancing since I was fourteen years old. I love it; but I usually go to the Institute across the main road." And Janie glanced shyly at the young man, deeming it unnecessary to mention the church dances.

"Oh! Is it good there? We usually come here because we learnt to dance here and we feel 'at home' so to speak. Where did you learn to dance?"

"Nowhere in particular; just picked it up; at church socials mostly, but practice makes perfect, doesn't it?" "Yes! I think you would like the instruments in the band. But, I like it here very much; it's very cosy."

The band finished the dance amid a loud round of applause, and as Janie was escorted back to her seat by her companion, he remarked:

"By the way, my name is Peter Ingram! What is yours?"

"Jane Pullen. Oh, here are the others! Thank you for asking me to dance!" replied Janie; not forgetting to be courteous.

When they reached the seats, Peter introduced his partner to his friend. "Jane Pullen – John Bailey." Janie offered her hand to the tall, dark young man. He took it and pressed it slightly, while he gazed intently at the flushed young face. Embarrassed, she withdrew her hand, feeling somehow that she had met this young man somewhere before. Then, remembering Nora at her side, she introduced her to Peter.

There were no spare chairs near, so the young men, murmuring their thanks, made their way back to their own seats.

"How did you get on?" Janie asked Nora.

"Oh, all right!" replied Nora, without enthusiasm, "but he's a bit stiff, as though he's having a lesson, and he kept staring round the room, looking for somebody. I'm sure he was watching you and his friend."

"Nonsense! Why should he be? Anyhow, I seem to know him; do you remember meeting him before?"

But Nora shook her head, not caring to pursue the subject.

Dance after dance, Janie whirled around the room with her new-found partner. Never could she remember enjoying herself so much. Nora grew more satisfied and gayer as different young men asked her to dance. They sat chattering, waiting for the interval waltz to begin. They both knew that ball-room etiquiette demanded that the male partner should invite his lady partner to have refreshments with him after that particular dance. And Janie was looking forward to the opportunity of closer social contact with Peter Ingram, whom she realised she liked very much.

Then the unexpected happened. The two girls could see Peter and John across the room and they appeared to be arguing. Then John put a hand in his pocket, withdrew it, and tossed something in the air. "Good gracious!" exclaimed Nora, "they are tossing up for something; I wonder what it can be?"

"I'm sure I don't know, but I don't suppose it's anything to do with us." But Janie puckered her brow as she felt she saw a tiny cloud on her horizon.

The band commenced to play the lilting 'Skater's Waltz'. The two young men made their way sharply across the floor and John Bailey planted himself firmly in front of Janie. "Miss Pullen, may I have this dance?" he inquired. Janie was dumbfounded and bitterly disappointed. She rose slowly to her feet and without a word or a smile glided off with her tall partner, while out of the corner of her eye she noticed Peter pair off with Nora.

Nora was right, John Bailey was not such a good dancer. For some reason he danced rather stiffly, while the hand that held hers was stretched far too high in the air. With a gesture of annoyance Janie jerked it to a more comfortable position, although she had to admit to herself that his other arm held her firmly and securely. He glanced down at her, sensing her annoyance, a half smile on his lips. "All right?" he inquired. "Yes, thank you!" but Janie did not smile. She gazed at him, a trifle contemptuously, and she noted how pale he was, his luxuriant dark hair intensifying the pallor. Her heart softened a little; perhaps he had been ill and that accounted for his dancing being somewhat awkward. He was very good-looking too, in a way. He had good features, and white even teeth, the smallest Janie had ever seen in a man. "Something worrying you?" he asked again, feeling her gaze upon him.

Janie flushed, feeling embarrassed. "Oh, I just wondered if you had been ill, you seem so pale and – and you dance a bit – bit – "Janie's voice trailed off; she did not know how to put it. She felt very uncomfortable. Her partner laughed and pressed her closer to him. "So you've noticed my gammy leg! Yes! I've had several operations on it – nearly lost it – spent three months in hospital; getting better now, though a bit stiff – guess that will wear off in time. Sorry, if my danc-ing isn't up to standard."

Janie was all apologies, and for the first time she smiled at him. "You know, you are very pretty when you smile; you should do it more often." His voice was half teasing, half tender.

Janie felt a warm glow inside her, and giving herself up to the dance and the strains of the beautiful melody, she did her best to harmonise her steps to those of her partner. But she still wished it had been Peter, and once, when they came close to him and Nora, she felt his eyes on her and her heart thrilled.

The waltz was over, and a general move was made towards the refreshment room. John Bailey suggested that the two girls hurry to secure a table, while he and Peter fetched the coffee. The two girls looked around and noticed that most of the tables were taken, then seeing one unoccupied over on the far side of the room, Janie made a 'bee-line' for it, with Nora close to her heels. They reached the table, just as a young man came up to it. Janie sat down firmly on a chair, while hastily pushing Nora into another, then firmly held on to the two vacant chairs. The young man looked at her questioningly, chagrin on his face.

"Sorry! This table is taken," remarked Janie defiantly, "we were here first." "That's open to question," the young man said rudely. John and Peter arrived on the scene, each carrying a tray on which were coffee and cakes.

"Anything wrong?" asked John, looking from the girls to the angry young man. "No," said Janie, "we just got the last table." John moved to set the tray on the table; at the same time the stranger turned to leave and as he passed John, Janie saw him deliberately lift his elbow to tip the tray. All the contents spilt into her lap, the hot coffee scalding her arm.

With a cry of pain she jumped to her feet, sweeping the crockery onto the floor. John whipped out his handkerchief, wiped the arm dry, then bound it up.

"I'm so sorry!" he said, "I can't think what happened, I'm not usually so care-less. I think you had better go to the cloakroom attendant, she has a first aid box – she will help you."

"I'll come with you," Nora exclaimed, jumping to her feet. "My goodness! Some mothers do have them – couldn't carry a tray properly! Just look what a mess she's in." And Nora glared angrily at John.

"No, no!" cried Janie, "it wasn't his fault, it was just an accident. Don't worry, please, John, I'll be all right."

But John was worried and embarrassed. The incident had spoiled the even-ing and it was only half over. With his arm around Janie's shoulders, he escorted the girls to the cloakroom. Then sitting on a chair outside the door, he prepared to wait for them.

The woman attendant was sympathetic and helpful; she soon had the scalded arm dressed and bandaged and the wet dress and under-slip over the back of the chair in front of a brisk coal-fire.

Janie sat miserably wrapped in her coat, wondering whatever Mom would say about the spoiled dress. She was sure that stain would never come out. Nora sat holding forth on the utter carelessness of men and of John Bailey in particular.

Janie remembered that her friend had not noticed the elbow tip the tray. She proceeded to give her the details, and Nora's indignation knew no bounds. "Why on earth didn't you tell John?" she exploded, "He would have given that chap what for." "Really! Nora, use your common sense – that's just why I didn't say anything. I didn't want to be the cause of a fight. Still, I didn't bargain for this!" Janie looked apprehensively at her arm and the spoiled garments.

At last, the dress was dry, but it looked very sad with the brown stain running all down the mauve silk front. Janie's eyes filled with tears as she beheld the sorry state. Quickly dressing, she put on her coat and hat. "Come on, Nora," she exclaimed, "I'm going home, I've had enough." "But the dance isn't over yet," Nora protested, "besides, I want to see Peter again." Suddenly Janie was angry. "Oh, very well, do as you like; stay if you want to, but I'm going home. I wish to goodness I hadn't listened to you in the first place, I wouldn't be in this mess now."

"Oh, Janie, be fair; I didn't know this was going to happen, and I don't want to stay without you." So saying, poor Nora, her face flushed with annoyance and disappointment, reluctantly changed her shoes and donned her hat and coat. Janie again thanked the attendent for her help and opening the door promptly ran into John Bailey waiting outside. "Oh, you are not going home," he exclaimed, noticing the outdoor clothes, "it's quite early yet."

"I'm sorry, John, yes – but I can't possibly go in the dance room in this dress, it's quite spoiled – anyway I don't feel like dancing now. Maybe we'll see you some other time, somewhere." And Janie's voice trailed off; she felt rather vague and a bit spiteful, she knew she was making excuses, and by the hurt look in the young man's eyes, he knew it too. Janie couldn't face him, she fiddled with her gloves and turned away. John caught hold of her arm. "Janie, if you must go, please, let me take you home; I've got a motor-cycle, could you ride pillion?" "I've ridden on my brother's bike! But, please, don't worry about me, I haven't far to go, I'd rather walk with my friend – there's no need for you to spoil your evening."

"It's already spoiled," John replied curtly, "At least, let me make amends; I should like to buy you another dress, will you accept it?" Janie looked quickly at him; again, she had that feeling that she had met him before. But, she knew, had she done so, she could never have forgotten him; his was a very striking personality. Her own attitudes puzzled her.

"No, no," she said, hastily, "my Mother would never allow me to accept a dress off a man, especially a stranger – but thank you all the same."

"I just want to replace the dress I've ruined, I promise, there's no strings attached," and the young man scowled, very exasperated.

Nora tittered, and Janie, glaring angrily at her, saw her expression change, while her eyes lit up and the colour flooded her cheeks. Looking in her direction, she saw Peter Ingram walking towards them. "What's happening?" he inquired, as he came up to them, his eyes on Janie.

"The girls are going home," John replied, "Would you like to take Nora, that's if she will ride pillion." Nora, her face beaming, assured them she would be delighted.

Janie, feeling cross and frustrated, turned silently away, towards the street door, Nora at her heels. The young men hastily retrieved their coats and cycle gear, and followed the girls outside. It was but a short distance to the street where Janie lived. At the top of the road Janie called to her driver to halt. After dismounting, she bade goodnight to John Bailey and called to Nora that she would see her as usual the next day. Then, nodding to Peter Ingram, she turned on her heel and sped away towards her home.

The house was empty, Mom and Dad being out for the evening. Janie was glad. After making herself a hot drink, she retired gratefully to bed, thankful to be closing the door on a miserable and disappointing evening.

Next morning, Mom was shown the coffee-stained dress and told how the accident happened. She examined Janie's arm and gave a 'tut-tut' of disapproval. "Really! Janie," she exclaimed, "I do hope there was no rough horseplay going on; what did the boy say and do I know him?"

"Boy." Janie was bewildered; you could hardly call John Bailey a boy and she was certain her Mother had never met him before. "Really, Mom," she retorted, "I don't dance with boys! John Bailey is a young man, he lives at Kings Heath – I don't know anything about him, it's the first time I have met him," and she looked knowingly at her sisters who stood nearby, ogling each other.

Mom looked her daughter over as though she was seeing her for the first time. "Young man, eh," she mused. "Will you be seeing him again?"

"No! Of course not, why should I?" and Janie turned crossly away, as she felt the hot colour rise to her cheeks.

"I see!" But Mom did not sound the least bit convinced. "There's only one thing to do; that dress must be dyed." "Dyed?" the triplets exclaimed in disbelief, "but what colour?" Mom hesitated. "Black, I think – Yes, black; it won't come out black, not a proper black, but at least it will get rid of the coffee stain."

Janie stared, and back over the years she watched as three pretty pink dresses were turned into a dismal array of mourning. She turned and ran for her bedroom as the hot tears scalded her eyes.

CHAPTER 6:

THE TALL DARK STRANGER.

Monday morning came, with all its preparations for work. Janie was dressing when Jessie excitedly burst into the room, waving a letter in her hand. "Post's arrived and there's a letter for you – who can it be from?"

"Don't be silly! It can't be for me, who would want to write to me?" Janie took the letter from her sister and gazed at the written address. "Miss Jane Pullen." Well, that was her, but she did not know the writing; firm well-written letters; she decided it was a man's hand.

"Well, open it, don't stare at it," said Jessie, impatiently, "Dad will be calling us in a minute, the tea is made."

Janie tore open the envelope and removed the folded paper. As she read the contents her eyes opened wide in astonishment.

> Dear Jane,
>
> I do hope your arm is better and that your Mother under-stood about the dress. Did you tell her I was quite willing to buy you another one? Please, will you meet me one evening to let me know what she said. We could go to see a film.
>
> Yours very sincerely,
> John Bailey.

"Oh-h-h-" Jessie gurgled, as she read the letter over Janie's shoulder. "He sounds nice; will you go?"

"Really, Jessie! It's no concern of yours, but I don't suppose I will. Now, please let me finish dressing or I'll be late for work."

Janie descended to the kitchen to find her Father drinking a cup of tea, while her Mother, as usual, was busy making sandwiches for her family to take to work, as there was no time to eat breakfast at home. "Who's been writing to you, then?" Mom enquired, without looking up. Janie held out the letter. "Here, read it, see what you think." Mom read it through slowly, then handed it to Dad.

"There's no need for him to buy a new dress," she said primly, "but he sounds a decent young man; you please yourself about meeting him. If you don't want to, just write and tell him so, don't keep him hanging about."

"How old is he and what's his job?" Dad enquired, giving back to the letter to his daughter.

"Dad! I only met him last night; there was no need to interrogate him." And Janie slammed her cup down irritably on its saucer.

"Oh, I see! He's not a regular at the church then?"

"Eh? Oh, no – he's never been to church. Is that the time? I'm going to be late for work." So saying Janie hastily put on her outdoor clothes, grabbed her sandwiches, called her goodbyes and rushed outside.

As she hurried along the streets, she felt self-reproachful that she had not told her parents the whole truth of how she had met John Bailey. Still, what did it matter now; nothing would come of it. She didn't intend to meet him again, decent or not. She decided he wasn't her sort. — Now, if it had been Peter, he was different; still, if she did go with him, it rather looked as if John Bailey would get in the way. She could not understand why Peter had danced with her several times, then handed her over to his friend for the interval waltz. She still felt sore about it. Perhaps he had not liked her dancing at all.

The girls who were at the dance grouped together talking, as Janie walked to her machine. Ada called across to her, "What became of you Saturday night, did you go off with the dark handsome stranger; aren't you lucky meeting him?"

"Lucky? I certainly wasn't lucky. I had the tray of refreshments thrown into my lap – my dress is spoiled, I went home."

The girls came over to hear the details, and Janie told them about John Bailey's letter, and how she had decided not to meet him again. Perhaps we all need a push to set us on the right road towards our Destiny. It seems that that role had fallen to Ada, who had chatted to her at the dance, and who had seen her with John Bailey. She looked closely at Janie. "Think it over, Jane," she said, "don't do anything hasty; he seemed a very nice fellow; at least, you could meet him once and see how you get on." She turned away, then added, "I wish I had the chance."

Janie was astonished; she began to feel rather a privileged person. But there was no time to say more as the machinery was switched on. She thought over her problem several times during the day. She had to admit that, had she never met Peter, his friend would have proved an attraction. She felt she was making rather too much importance of the whole matter. No doubt, John Bailey would come and pass like a ship in the night; nothing could come of one visit to the cinema. She had plenty of time to become serious over one fellow, no matter how attractive he was; when she was twenty-six she would think about it. That was a sensible age, thought Janie, when one could think seriously of settling down.

During her dinner break she penned a short polite note to John Bailey, thanking him for his letter, and suggesting the coming Saturday evening for a visit to the cinema – she would meet him at the top of her street at 6.30 pm. She posted it on the way back to work and immediately wished she had not done so;

why on earth did she let other people talk her into doing something she really did not want to do?

On Friday evening the three sisters went as usual to the church drama group, and were met by Nora James, who seemed to be bubbling over with news and excitement. After a few words to Jessie and Julie, she drew Janie aside. "All set for Saturday evening then?" she asked, a huge smile lighting up her face.

Janie was startled. "What on earth do you mean, who told you about Saturday?"

"Peter Ingram, of course. He wrote to me and invited me to make up a foursome with you and his friend to the film show; I believe they mean to take us up town. We'll have a grand time."

Once again Janie felt cross and irritable. "So you think," she retorted. "Well, I don't! I wish I hadn't agreed to go; I'm fed up with the whole business."

"Really, Janie! What on earth's wrong with you? It's about time we had a couple of sensible chaps to take us out. We are getting a bit above those Sunday school boys – I'm fed up with them."

Janie opened her mouth to respond with a cutting reply, but, noting her friend's hurt expression, changed her mind and turned away. Poor Nora! She couldn't help it if Peter preferred her company, and evidently she was thrilled at the thought of going out with him.

When Saturday evening arrived, Janie dressed with extra care, donning the new blue 'in-between seasons' dress that Mom had made for each of her girls. She carefully pulled the small brimmed hat low over her brow and noted with satisfaction how her blonde hair curled becomingly in the nape of her neck and around her ears. A wine coloured flannel coat completed the ensemble and as she stepped back to survey her reflection in the mirror, Janie felt confident and ready to face any ordeal that might arise.

Mom looked her over critically when she descended to the living room. Warm approval showed in her eyes, also a wistful yearning that made Janie feel a little sad. Did Mom realise that evening that one of her girls at least, was fast leaving her girlhood behind and emerging excitedly into womanhood? She quickly shook the mood away and smoothed down her white apron. "Now, behave yourself and don't be late home," she ordered curtly, then hesitantly, "Have a nice time."

Janie impulsively caught hold of her mother and kissed her. "No! I won't be late, Mom, don't worry. Bye Dad!" "Bye you two, remember me to the crowd at the dance," and she tittered merrily as she noted her father's open-mouthed interest and her sisters' knowing grins. As she closed the door behind her, her father's belated instructions reached her ears.

"Don't you be late in – now mind my girl!" he called. And, smiling again, she ran lightly down the entry.

*   *   *

When she reached her rendezvous, Janie found John and Peter waiting. They looked neat and sombre in their navy blue gabardine raincoats and soft turn-down trilbys. She noted the look of admiration from both pairs of eyes as they greeted her and she turned away with embarrassment, glad to see Nora come tripping up to them.

John took hold of her arm and led her over to the tram-stop, Peter and Nora came close on their heels. The tram was pretty crowded so the four were not able to sit together. The two girls sat near to each other at the back, while the two young men found seats further down the tram. This gave Janie the opportunity to study her partner for the evening. His face was still pale and in rather serious mood, making him appear older than she at first thought. While she still mused, wondering why she still had that feeling that she had met him before, he suddenly jerked around and looked straight into her eyes. His whole face lit up in a friendly smile, and with an inward gasp she realised he was very good-looking and perhaps not so old as she had at first thought. She gave a half smile in return and dropped her gaze shyly.

The evening passed very pleasantly, and Janie realised she had enjoyed herself, so much so that when John suggested a further meeting the next day to "have a spin out into the country on the motor-cycles," she did not demur.

And so the time passed pleasantly enough. It was the sewing factory's very busy period, and Janie worked very hard at "piece-work"; the harder he worked, the more money she earned. She did not mind, as the days passed quickly and Saturday soon came with its visit to the cinema or to one of the select dance halls in the city centre. John and Peter seemed bent on giving the girls a good time and as all four got on well together the evenings grew gay and happy.

Janie found it hard to determine her feelings concerning the two young men. Her heart still warmed towards Peter and she told herself it was because of him that she looked forward to their meetings. And yet, when she was dancing with him, his arms holding her close, her eyes would wander around the room, looking for John who was dancing with Nora. That young lady enjoyed herself immensely; she never stopped chattering and giggling, and Janie felt sometimes that she got on their partners' nerves. She knew she got on hers; after all, she ought to show some decorum and not behave incessantly like an excited school-girl.

Then one Friday evening Nora was absent from the church drama group. Janie did not worry; she knew she would be seeing her on the Saturday evening, and in any case if she did not happen to turn up, it would only take a few moments to go to her home to see if she were ill. But when Janie arrived at the usual meeting place, she found John waiting alone. She looked about her in astonishment, "Why, where's Nora and Peter?" she inquired.

"I don't think Peter will be coming with us again, at least not with Nora. I'm afraid she isn't really his kind of girl and it's no use him continuing seeing her if he's not really keen. He's written to her to explain," and John's voice trailed off rather awkwardly.

Janie felt bewildered. Poor Nora! How disappointed she must be; she liked Peter so much and enjoyed the free weekends they had all spent together. She would pop in to see her tomorrow.

John's voice broke in on her thoughts. "Shall we go to the 'Futurist'? You don't mind coming alone with me, do you?" He sounded rather anxious.

Janie smiled. "No, of course not! And I don't mind where we go."

He took her hand and pulled it gently through his arm and smiled reassuringly at her as he pressed it to his side. She forgot her rather troubled thoughts as she noted his tender gaze and gave herself up to the feeling of contentment that pervaded her.

That night he kissed her "Goodnight" for the first time when he saw her home. And Janie did not mind.

CHAPTER 7:

SUNDAY TEA CEREMONY.

Next morning at breakfast, Dad asked Janie how her new friendship was going on. She explained how Peter and Nora had broken up the foursome the evening before and how she and John had gone alone to the cinema.

"Oh!" Dad looked across knowingly at Mom, then back again to his daughter; surveying her solemnly he stated, "Then I think it's about time me and Mother met him. Ask him to have a cup of tea with us next Sunday afternoon."

Janie felt rather doubtful, this was rather rushing things. She wasn't sure she wanted John to meet her family yet; she would rather get to know him better first.

"I'll think about it," she said, "he may not want to come; after all, we've only known each other a short time."

"There's no harm in asking him," Dad insisted, "I'd like to see the fellow you're going out with; if he doesn't want to meet your parents, you'd best give him his marching orders."

Janie was indignant. "Really, Dad! How you talk; we are only friends. Marching orders, indeed!" Her voice trailed off hopelessly; she was lost for words. But Dad was firm, and by the look on Mom's face, she agreed with him.

"Well, you can bring your friends home for a cup of tea; we'll always make them welcome. So don't forget, next Sunday."

Julie and Jessie were delighted; they smiled at one another and beamed at their sister. At last they would meet the young man who had been taking her out and giving her a good time. Also, it was nice to know that Mom and Dad did not mind them having a young man friend and were prepared to welcome him home.

So the next time Janie met John, she gave him Dad's invitation. He hesitated a moment, then said: "Do you want me to come, Janie?" His voice sounded rather anxious. Janie was surprised and rather puzzled. "Why of course," she replied, "I would like you to meet my parents."

The following Sunday afternoon John presented himself to the Pullen household. Janie introduced him all round and as he shook hands with her mother, he noted the rather anxious gaze from the tired brown eyes. He gave her a reassuring smile and was pleased to see an answering gleam chase away the anxiety. He liked the little family right away, although the sight of Julie and Jessie gave him a turn. They were so identical, and yet so different to Janie – for triplets they were an odd trio.

While the family talked to their guest to make him feel 'at home', Janie busied herself in the kitchen, making tea and slicing the fruit cake she had made the day before.

John stayed a good couple of hours; and he talked most of the time. Janie learnt more of him and his family in that space of time, than she had known all the time she had been going out with him. He had a good job as foreman electrician with one of the oldest established contractors in the city. He lived in a nice suburb, with his father and two spinster sisters, who were quite a few years older than him. His mother had died when he was fourteen years old. Janie noticed how his voice lowered as he spoke of her, while a shadow of sadness crossed his face. He had felt her loss deeply and he still missed her. Janie gazed at him with a new interest.

It was quite apparent that Dad was smitten with him. He listened to the details of the various contracts he had worked on, with a growing admiration. Mom gazed at him with a somewhat puzzled expression on her face, while Jessie and Julie stared in silent admiration – Janie had never known them so quiet.

At last John glanced at his wristwatch and rose to his feet. "I must be going," he said, "Thank you for inviting me, I have enjoyed meeting you all, very much." He shook hands with them all round. Mom murmured her pleasure at meeting him and hoped he would visit again. Dad shook his hand heartily and welcomed him into the bosom of his family.

Janie felt a little bewildered by it all, she felt that fate was rather pushing her along. She went to see John off and arranged to meet him again, but this time he said he would call for her. When she returned to the house, she found her sisters had broken their long silence and were chattering excitedly. Dad said, "He seemed a nice young man, but most important of all, he's got a good job and an excellent trade in his fingers." Mom said she liked him very much. He had very good manners and appeared well brought up, but she wished he wouldn't talk so fast and cut his words short, she hadn't understood much of what he said.

"Oh," said Julie, "I expect that was because he was nervous and after all, he was, sort of, on show."

"Oh!" breathed Jessie, her eyes shining, "what does that matter? He's so good looking; so tall and handsome – that thick black hair, with those wonderful blue eyes."

Janie stared at her family in wonderment; they were presenting John Bailey to her in a new light. "Tall and handsome – black hair and wonderful blue eyes." She had never noticed. Next time she met him she would certainly look.

CHAPTER 8:

MAKING A MATCH OF IT.

So Janie looked and wondered. Why had she been so slow in noticing the charms of this young man? He was not only good to look at, but it was a pleasure to be in his company; he knew so much about most things and had a strong sense of humour. He seemed more at ease with Janie since Nora and Peter had given up going out with them. He had lost that rather Victorian politeness. Peter! Of course! Janie mused; he was the reason she would not let herself get interested in John Bailey. She remembered the slight figure, sparkling eyes ad the gay, easy smile. He had held her close when they danced and pressed her hand when he returned her to her seat. And often when the four of them were waiting for seats at the cinema or to be served in a restaurant, she would glance in his direction to find him gazing at her, and his expression would bring the colour flooding to her cheeks. She knew he and John were the best of friends, and had been since schooldays. They only lived a few doors from each other, and spent time together when John didn't see her.

She was still puzzled why Peter had not asked her to dance the interval waltz on that first evening they met. Once, when she and John were talking over some of the outings they had shared with Nora and Peter, she decided to ask him if he could clear up the mystery. John looked at her with surprise, then laughed teasingly. "Why yes, of course," he said, "I wanted the dance with you, so did Peter; so we tossed up for it and poor old Peter lost." Then noting her expression of not knowing whether to be cross or pleased, he put his arm around her waist and drew her to him, "You know, Jane, Fate spun that coin for me – we are meant for each other, you and I. I knew it, the first moment I set eyes on you – I've never met a girl yet, who affects me as you do. Somehow, I feel we've always been together, and always will be."

Janie looked up into the blue eyes and her own filled with tears. What John said and the way he said it affected her strangely. Perhaps, in the long distant past, they had been together. What had her beloved Grandfather told her – that there were more things in Heaven and Earth than we ever dreamed of – that somewhere, there were other worlds? Surely, if we had lived in them, we must have known people, loved ones, whom we knew and loved in this life. And the way she and John had been thrown together was, to say the least, very odd.

John noticed her emotion, and very gently he kissed her on her quivering lips. A warm glow filled her heart and with a natural impulse, she returned his kiss. Janie felt that at last her eyes and heart had been opened; to be without John now would be unbearable – he had grown very dear to her.

"There is something I must tell you, Jane. I have been engaged before; but it didn't work out. We got bored with each other and quarrelled a lot. Six months before you and I met, we decided to part – how glad I am that we did! Meeting you, Jane, has made me realise that I never really loved Vera. I liked her very much, but I can see that that is no basis for marriage. She grew very moody and discontented; I could never please her. I suppose I got on her nerves. Anyway, it was a great relief when I didn't have to see her anymore."

Janie stared at the young man without speaking. Again that tantalizing feeling that she had met him before flitted across her memory; something he had just said had brought it to the surface. She tried to hold it, to analyse it, but to no purpose; once again it evaded her.

"It's really nothing to do with me," she said at last. "It happened before you met me. Still, I am glad you told me – "she hesitated, not quite knowing how to say it, "If, at any time, you decide you'd rather go back to her, you will tell me, won't you?"

"Jane, I mean it when I tell you that part of my past is quite over; even had I never met you, I should never have gone back. You are the only girl for me. You must believe that, sweetheart."

Janie was only too happy to believe it. A new world of being loved and of loving was opening up for her and she gave herself up to the joy in her heart, and the thought of the rosy future, where she and John Bailey would always be together.

A few weeks later, the young couple were walking in the shopping centre near John's home, when Janie noticed two young women walking towards them. The youngest-looking of the two seemed vaguely familiar to her; suddenly, she remembered. The button factory and Mary Harper. Three years had gone by since that eventful period, and this was the first time she had met her one-time friend. "Why!" she exclaimed to John, "here is an old friend of mine, I haven't seen her for three years, I must have a word with her." She glanced hurriedly at John and saw that he also had recognised the two girls and was staring at them with a set white face.

The four met and Janie and Mary greeted each other warmly; then through the excited chatter, Janie heard John's voice, strained and distant, "Hello, Vera, how are you?" The older girl replied in a low voice. Janie stopped chattering and looked at the two with a puzzled air. Mary, quick to size up the situation, introduced her friend to her sister. Janie took the offered hand and looked into cold grey eyes. Vera seemed years older than she and Mary; her whole demeanour was cold and unbending; her attire dark and sombre, giving her an age that belied the pale young face.

Janie's thoughts were in a whirl. She could not join in the conversation. Her mind went back to the 'button factory' days, with the lunchtimes spent in the park and Mary Harper's chatter of her sister Vera's rather stormy engagement to a young electrician named John Bailey. So that was the reason for the feeling of having met John before. Janie was astounded at the tricks Fate could play on unsuspecting human beings. She knew of the one man in her life, three years before she actually met him. And now, looking at Vera with her dull aloofness, she knew for certain that John could never go back to her. Her only wonder was how he could ever have thought of marrying her.

CHAPTER 9:

EARLY MARRIED LIFE.

Janie could not sleep. For some reason she felt queer and strange – a little afraid. John lay at her side, sleeping soundly, and not wishing to disturb him, she gently put back the bedclothes and slipped out of bed. Wrapping herself in her dressing gown, she went to the window and drew back the curtain a little so that she might look out.

Sitting on a chair, she surveyed the moonlit world beyond. The green golf-course opposite had turned into a silvery lake, while the trees at its edges looked like ghostly figures wearing large feathery hats, swaying to the rhythm of the whispering wind. In the distance, an owl cried out plaintively like an earthbound soul calling for help.

Janie shivered and drew her robe closely around her. She could not understand her strange mood; apprehension made her feel breathless and tense. The child she was carrying was not due for another month, if then. The doctors at the hospital seemed doubtful as to when the pregnancy would end, and had only given her an approximate date. Her mind went back over the last ten months, to the day she and John were married. All the rush and excitement, the wellwishers and the reporters and crowds of sightseers, both at the house and church alike. It isn't every day that triplets are involved in a wedding. Janie looked radiant in the white lace dress that Mom had made, and the long silk veil with the orange blossom head dress (so John had declared). Julie and Jessie, resplendent in oyster lace and petunia coloured taffeta, with large floppy hats, acted as bridesmaids. Mom had wept and Dad had choked on his speech at the small reception held in the polished parlour at home.

John's two sisters and father were there, and Janie glanced rather anxiously at them from time to time. She wondered what they thought of her rather humble home. Then looking round at the highly polished furniture, the brasses glittering in the hearth, the sedately patterned lino, with the new cherry-red hearthrug and the rosewood piano gleaming in its place, she decided that her home might be humble, but at least it was clean and attractive.

Of course, she had met the sisters several times when visiting John's home and was becoming more used to them. Liz, the eldest, was ten years older than her brother, while Floss was eighteen months younger than her sister. Both had thick black hair which they wore in a bun at the nape of the neck; Liz was tallish and thin, while Floss was short and inclined to plumpness. Janie liked Liz very much, she was so gay and friendly and her blue eyes twinkled merrily when she laughed. With Floss, she felt a rather reserved aloofness, as though she was reluctant to become too friendly. Liz mentioned once that Vera Harper was a friend of some years standing to Floss – indeed, that was how John had met her in the first place. So Janie realised the reason for the coldness. She decided to ignore Floss's attitude, and was always pleasant and friendly towards her.

John's father was a quiet educated man, who had a good position in a local bakery. He always worked nights, so Janie had seen very little of him, but the little she had seen, she liked very much.

John had told him of his engagement to Janie on her twentieth birthday, and when Janie had showed him her lovely ring, he had taken her hand and wished her every happiness and told her he was glad his son had chosen her.

The following July they were married, and in January, when Janie knew for sure she was pregnant, her father-in-law had died from the cancer that had made him so ill for the last weeks of his life.   .

The young couple had found rooms in a quiet house, just around the corner from John's home; it was in a pleasant position opposite the golfing green, and Janie loved the semi-seclusion and the country aspect.

A yellow glow in the distant sky warned her that dawn was breaking, but still she sat on, reluctant to move, lest she disturb the peace that had settled about her, like a soft warm blanket. She no longer felt afraid; her soul had reached out for help and unseen arms held her close.

When John woke, Janie told him she thought she ought to go to the hospital or at least see a doctor. Alarmed, he dressed hastily, then ran down the road to the phone kiosk. Janie dressed, made sure all the things she needed to take to the hospital were in the suitcase, and by the time she had made the bed, her husband had returned.

"Are you all right; are you ready?" he asked breathlessly. "The hospital say you must go right away, so I've phoned for a taxi; it will be here in twenty minutes." Janie smiled at his consternation. "Mrs. Willis has made us a pot of tea; you must have some breakfast before you go, there will be time."

Janie was examined in the receiving department of the hospital, and the doctor decided she should be admitted. John saw her alone for a few moments before she was taken up to the maternity ward. His face was pale and anxious. "I do wish it hadn't happened like this," he said, "I do hope everything will be all right. You know I shall be thinking of you all the time you are here." He hesitated, then drawing her to him, "You know, Jane, I love you very much; please come back to me."

Janie felt choked; she remembered her apprehension during the night and the doctor's slight frown of preoccupation after he had examined her. But her naturally bright nature came to her aid, "You mustn't worry, John," she said, "I'm sure everything will be very easy; why, I'm no size at all, I must be having a small baby and they say they are the best to have." "I hope so, sweetheart, I'll try not to worry," he kissed her tenderly. "On my way to work I'll pop in and

let your Mother know."
   The nurse arrived to take Janie up to the ward and John took his departure.

CHAPTER 10:

ASTRAL ADVENTURE.

The day passed slowly in examinations and tests, while her aching body cried out for sleep. But when night-time came, Janie lay wide awake. The sister on her rounds spoke quietly to her, then sent her accompanying nurse away on an errand. When she returned, Janie was given hot milk and two tablets, and after a while, feeling soothed and relaxed, she felt into a fitful sleep.

Next morning, after the usual preliminaries of a maternity ward, the sister advised Janie to put on her dressing gown and go with two more patients to sit out on the balcony in the warm sunshine. She was glad of the change, even though she felt dizzy and her legs seemed loath to move, she donned her robe with some difficulty and proceeded to follow her two companions.

Halfway across the room, a searing pain shot through her body and something seemed to give way. A warning shout from a cleaner who was mopping the polished floor made Janie stop in her tracks and look back. Little pools of blood ran on the floor where she had walked; looking down, she saw more dripping round her feet. Stupidly she gazed round, not knowing what to do; her head swam and she felt sick. Dimly she was aware of a figure hurrying towards her; and of strong arms holding her safe as she sank into the dark void of unconsciousness.

When she awoke, she was lying on a medical couch in a large clinical room, with the midwife and nurse fussing over her. "What is happening?" she asked weakly, "why all that blood?"

"There, there, dear, m'dear, no need to worry; you've had a haemorrhage: Baby won't be long now; isn't that nice?"

"But it's on the eighth month, surely something's wrong?"

"Tut, tut, it's not unusual; these things do happen. Don't worry your pretty head about it; if baby decided to arrive, there's nothing we can do about it. You just do what you're told and everything will be all right."

But baby did not arrive as quickly or as easily as the midwife predicted. For sixty-two hours Janie fought and struggled when the pain rent her body. As the hours dragged slowly by, nurse and midwife were changed, different voices instructed and comforted her.

The sister popped in now and again to see how things were. Once, Janie heard her enquire, "The water – hasn't it broken yet? – It has? – Good heavens, a dry labour – no wonder, all this time; poor child!" During a quiet period, when she could think, her thoughts turned to John – what was he doing – what was he thinking; would she ever see him again? had he had a premonition when he said, "Jane, come back to me."

Once, through her pain, she heard his voice outside the door, "I must see her; do you hear? I must see for myself how she is. All this time! It's dreadful." In a little while, when she was getting her breath back, sister came in, carrying a bunch of beautiful golden roses.

"My dear," she said, "your husband has brought you these – aren't they lovely? Now, he insists on seeing you, but he is not allowed in here, it would not be safe. We must take you to another room. If we move you now as you are, there is a great risk you may lose your life or you will certainly lose your baby. We have decided to leave the decision to you."

Janie looked up into the anxious eyes staring down at her, and suddenly she felt that all this was unreal. Surely she would wake up to find she had come through an awful nightmare. She lifted her hand to touch the roses, but found she hadn't the strength. She was so weary; if she could have slept, she knew she would not have awakened in this world. "Tell me the truth, sister," she whispered, "I am not having a baby, am I? There's something else wrong with me."

A startled expression flitted across the older woman's face; her concern made her voice sharp. "Tut, tut, mother, what fancies you have, that little one will be here soon; wait until you hear it cry, you will know you have a baby then." She lowered her tone, "Now about your husband – what shall I tell him?"

The pain was starting again. Janie shook her head. "No! No!" she cried, "I mustn't see him, I can't let him see me like this; but give him my love, tell him I will come back to him."

About ten hours later, Janie's son was born. She lay back weak and exhausted, unable to open her eyes, vaguely aware that some commotion was going on between the midwife and her two nurses. She had heard that babies cry as soon as they are born, but apart from some subdued mutterings and sharp smacks, there was silence in the room. "Harder than that, nurse, a really good one, you must get him moving – here, let me try."

Janie was suddenly afraid. Something was wrong. She vainly tried to call out, to ask what was amiss, but her voice had lost its power. Then, a real good slap and a sharp shake and the infant's protesting cry filled the room.

"Thank God," breathed the Staff Nurse, "now,, if you can carry on, I'll get back to the ward." The midwife focussed her attention on the young mother who lay, violently shivering. "There, there," she comforted, "we'll soon have you tidied up and tucked up in a nice warm bed – "

Janie felt that she had never been so cold and so tired; her head was swimming from lack of sleep, her eyes burning with the strain of keeping awake for so long. Her body felt numb; whatever the midwife was doing to her, caused no sensation to her in her strange condition. Then she felt a tug, and a warm caress crept slowly up her back and embraced her shoulders. "Oh! That's lovely and warm," she murmured, lifting up her hand to see why it felt wet. Something red was dripping from it – her eyes blurred as she tried to concentrate – she felt sick and terribly dizzy and as she sank down into awful darkness she heard a distressed cry, "Nurse, nurse for God's sake!"

Janie felt as free as a bird as she felt herself rising up, buoyant and carefree, glad to be finished with pain and weariness. Her feet touched solid ground, and opening her eyes she gazed around her. To her amazement she was still in the "labour ward", but she had somehow left her bed and had floated up to the ceiling.

Voices reached her and looking down she saw the midwife shaking something that lay on the bed, while she called out to it, "Mother, mother! For goodness' sake open your eyes – nurse – phone Doctor Mackenzie – tell him the baby is born, but the mother has had a severe haemorrhage; he must come quickly. Mother, mother!," and the shaking grew more vigorous.

Janie watched the nurse leave the room and heard her running feet in the corridor outside. She heard the click and burr of the telephone and the nurse's urgent voice as she spoke to someone at the other end. The receiver clattered down and the running footsteps returned. "He will not come; he says he does not attend the mother after the baby has been born."

"Stupid man! Doesn't he realize the mother is dying – in fact, I think she may have gone; I can't get her to open her eyes – Run and see if Doctor Cameron is on call, she may have come back from leave by now – but please hurry!"

Janie found it all very interesting, although very puzzling. She heard a sound behind her and looked round. A wonderful silver light shed its rays all about that part of the room, blotting out the walls and ceiling. Suddenly, the light formed into a narrow corridor and a figure came hurriedly down. As it drew near, Janie saw a man with white longish hair and beard. The face was fresh and young, yet there was an air of age about it. But the eyes made her gasp. They were the most wonderful she had ever seen – full of love, kindness and an ageless wisdom. He was dressed in a white robe, with a golden girdle at the waist, while in his hand he carried a golden staff.

He came up to the astonished girl and spoke quickly. "My dear, you must go back, go now – we are not ready for you yet, go quickly."

"But I don't want to go back to all that," and she pointed to the scene below, "please, let me stay here."

"No, no! You will regret it later, there's so much for you to do. I promise, there will be no more pain; I will help you to get well. Go! Go, now, before it's too late." And Janie felt his hand at her back, urging her forward.

"Who are you? Please tell me your name?" As she floated swiftly downwards the voice rang in her ears, "I am Joseph."

"Thank God!" the midwife breathed, as the young mother opened her eyes, "I thought you had gone." "I did go," Janie explained, "but the old man sent me back." "Old man! What old man?" "Up there – on the ceiling. It was wonderful; he said I should get well – there would be no more pain but I'm so tired, please let me sleep," and the soft, weak voice trailed away into a deep sigh.

The midwife gave a startled glance to the nurse, who had come back in time to hear what their young patient had said, and both looked reluctantly at he ceiling, as though afraid of what they might see. Just then, the door opened and the doctor and her assistant hurried up to the bed. More nurses were sent for and so began to the struggle to stop the haemorrhage and save Janie's life.

In the days that followed, Janie thought often of her strange experience. She was in hospital for a month, confined to a small room by herself, and because she was extremely ill and weak, John was given a 'special pass' so that he could visit her each evening for half an hour.

On his first visit, Janie was terribly shocked when she saw him. His face was white and drawn, the eyes large and burning as though he had come through an intense fever. She realised she wasn't the only one who had experienced wakeful, suffering nights. She clasped his large hand closely to her, while the tears rained silently down her cheeks. Now she understood, in part, what Joseph had meant when he said she would regret it later, if he had allowed her to stay with him. She shuddered to think of John being given their fair-haired little son to take home alone and to bring up without her help.

She felt that somehow, she had always known the old-young man who had sent her back on her son's fateful birthday. Sent her back – from where? And how had she left her bed and risen up to the ceiling like she had done? She had been able to see and hear all that had gone on in the room below. She had never heard of Doctors Mackenzie or Cameron until that night.

Thinking of Joseph had brought to her mind that other lovable old man who had so much coloured her rather drab childhood. He had gone away for ever, or so she thought, but that wonderful vision she had of him on the day his 'body' was buried made her wonder if after all, something does happen to us at death, that the body in the grave is not the end.

When she told John of these things, he said she must have dreamt them; but she knew she wasn't asleep in the 'labour ward', or it was not a normal sleep – the midwife had said that she thought "her patient had gone." Gone where? Did she really mean that she thought she had died and that somehow she had left that pain-racked body on the bed and had floated away up to the ceiling, where Joseph had come and swiftly sent her back again? She remembered, also, the time the next-door neighbour had died, and about two weeks after the funeral, Janie had met her coming up the entry, when she, Janie, had bee going on an errand for Mom. She had forgotten all about her death, a child rarely keeps these things in mind, and she had spoken to her and receiving no answer, simply thought that Ma Bullock was sitting on her 'high horse'. However, when she reached the street, Janie's 'memory gates' had opened and she had rushed back to Mom in quite a state, wondering why she had just seen Ma Bullock who had been dead for two weeks. Of course, Mom had been quite startled, but she had handled the situation by declaring that her offspring was running a temperature and should be put to bed immediately with a cup of hot milk.

Grandad was quite different when she told him. He smiled at her in his kind gentle way, and said softly, "These things can and do happen, little Jane; a child's mind is clear and open and can perceive things unseen by older people. But try to forget about it until you are older and can understand it. If I am around I will try to explain all about it. If I am not, I am sure you will be brought into contact with someone who can help you. You know, child, in your search for knowledge, God usually sends along the right person to help you."

And that time when she worked in the button factory, and the unknown voice had saved her from a terrible death – and how had she escaped from the clutter of packing cases? Janie realised they were all strange and weird experiences; but somehow they were all related and she wondered who and where the person was, who would one day explain the mystery to her.

CHAPTER 11:

A PATHWAY TO TRUTH.

So life went on for Janie as she was happily occupied in bringing up her small son and making a comfortable home for her hardworking husband. Needless to say Mom and Dad and her two sisters were thrilled with little John Junior. His parents had fully intended to give him another name, but during the time he was in hospital the nurses called him "young John", and his mother grew used to it and was reluctant to change it.

John's sisters also were very fond of the baby, so Janie always found a 'baby sitter' when she and John wished to go out. After a while, the comfortable rooms were exchanged for a parlour-type council house on a pleasant estate about one and a half miles away.

One day, when young John was about two years old, the little family had called on Mom and Dad and were discussing the forthcoming Summer holiday. Dad, rather wistfully, remarked he would like to visit his twin brother, who years ago had married a Welsh girl and had settled in a little mountain village in South Wales. John, ever anxious to be helpful, suggested that he and Janie together with young John should take 'Ma and Pa' there on the motorcycle and sidecar he had acquired since the coming of his young son. Dad did not answer, but stared from one to another, his mouth open, while the colour mounted his cheeks, denoting to his amused daughter that his excitement was duly mounting.

Mom hesitated, then in a rather worried voice, "But John, do you think it will take us all? And we must take a bit of luggage, going for a week." "Of course it will take us all, Ma; why it's a good strong sidecar – you can sit in the main seat with baby on your lap, Jane at the small seat at the back – she's only a slip of a wench – and Pa on the pillion and the luggage in the grid at the back. Why that engine is five horse-power – quite sufficient to pull all us and our luggage."

Janie could not help but laugh at her mother's bewildered expression; she visualised her mental picture of five strapping horses pulling them all to the mountains of Wales. "Don't worry, Mom," she laughed, "if John says he'll take us all, he will, and we'll come to no harm. What do you say, Dad?" turning to her father, who by now was fairly bubbling with suppressed excitement, his face a rosy glow, in the centre of which his nose shone like a beacon on the headland.

"I think it a marvellous idea – John's right, he'll look after us. I'll send to our Bill and make the arrangements. I think we'll drink to it," and turning to the cupboard, he produced a bottle of light ale; pouring his wife a small glass, he proceeded to gulp down the rest with great relish, after toasting to the success of the coming holiday, Janie and John solemnly followed suit with their preferred cup of tea.

At last the great day arrived. With help from Julie and Jessie, the little family were safely packed into the sturdy sidecar; the luggage, strapped firmly to the grid, acted as a back-rest for Dad who perched proudly on the pillion, behind John's broad back. Amid laughing "goodbyes" and genial hand-waves from neighbours who had come out to see the family off, the loaded 'five horses' spluttered slowly off down the street, and as the engine grew warm, the speed settled down to a steady thirty miles an hour. The great city with its sprawling suburbs was gradually left behind, and Dad staring far ahead, mentally saw the mountains of Wales looming across the distant horizon.

It was a bright sunny day, and after reaching the country, several stops were made to rest the 'horses' and allow them to cool down, while the passengers refreshed themselves from Mom's generous picnic basket. All were happy and in high spirits; together they were exploring, for them, fresh fields, and the thought of the week ahead filled them all with a thrilled anticipation.

Evening was breathing her misty breath over the mountain tops which were now drawing near as the little party drove into "our Bill's village". The setting sun spread its rosy glory across the lower slopes of the granite masses, while from the tapestry of light and shade, golden pathways led upwards, to be lost in the caressing mist. Janie held her breath as she surveyed the majestic beauty, and once again her heart sped upwards to the dream-world beyond, and her unshed tears choked in her throat. The whole party were silent as they surveyed the wondrous sight, and though by now they were feeling sore and travel-weary, their spirits soared high as they felt that the mountains of Wales were sending them a special welcome.

And a warm welcome awaited them at their relative's home. After hugs and kisses all round, the travellers sat down to a tasty cooked meal, after which Dad, with tears in his eyes, ceremoniously thanked his son-in-law for their safe and sound arrival.

Janie was happy as she watched her husband and her father. She felt their week's holiday had got off to a good start.

The next day dawned bright and warm and after the breakfat things were cleared away, Brenda, Janie's cousin, offered to take the young couple on a tour of the village. Brenda was a tall, dark, attractive girl, about two years older than Janie; she was married and lived with her husband, Gein, two-year-old daughter Stella, and her mother and father, in a large stone-built house at the foot of the mountain. It seemed there was as much of a housing shortage here as in the larger towns, and, because coal-mining was the major industry and unemployment was high, the house-building programme was almost at a standstill through lack of funds.

Uncle Bill had his own small business as a tinsmith, making miner's lamp and all sorts of tin wares. At the moment his son-in-law was unemployed as a miner, and so helped him in his workshop in the large front room of the house.

After dinner, the clouds gathered and before tea-time rain was falling steadily. Aunt Pam gazed thoughtfully through the window at the frowning skies and the little rivers of water running down the yard from the weeping mountain slopes.

"Jane," she said, turning to her sister-in-law, "this evening you may as well go to the club with Bill and Bert and I'll take Janie and John to my meeting with me. Brenda will look after the babies, she likes to stay in and listen to the radio."

Brenda paused in her task of setting the table for tea and glanced out of the window at the wet scene beyond. "Isn't it rather wet to go traipsing all that way tonight?" she asked. "Tut! Tut! The young ones will enjoy it – they are not made of sugar, are they – they can put on their macs and over-shoes, can't they?" Aunt Pam's voice rose to a sharp shrill crescendo, as it always did when her wishes or suggestions were questioned. Young John looked up from his toys and stared at this new strange great-aunt with growing fear in his eyes. Janie saw the gesture and with a laugh swept her son up into her arms.

"Oh! I don't mind going out into the rain," she affirmed brightly, "but what meeting is this, Aunt? And you'd better ask John, he may not want to go." "He'll go and like it; and you'll find out what it's all about when you get there, so let's say no more and get the tea on," and Aunt Pam pursed her lips and strode off into the kitchen.

She was a straight well-built figure above medium height, with dark greying hair and penetrating blue eyes; her skin was smooth, with pale complexion and full red mouth. Janie thought in her youth she must have been very attractive, and she loved the way she laughed, which was quite often and Janie knew in spite of the sharp shrill Welsh voice, she had a heart of gold.

After tea, Janie prepared herself for the weather, while her husband went in search of his raincoat, the expression on his face clearly indicating he was humouring the whim of a mad woman. Young John was quite happy to play with his new playmate, Stella, so long as 'Auntie Brenda' stayed with them, and his terrifying Aunt Pam vanished from the scene.

The three went out into the rain, Aunt Pam brandishing the largest black umbrella that Janie had ever seen. She was instructed to keep up with her Aunt so that she would be under the shelter of the swaying umbrella, but in the end Janie had almost to run to keep up with the lightning strides of the older woman. John splashed his way along at their rear, his coat collar turned up close around his neck as the water ran in little rivulets from the brim of his trilby hat.

The quiet streets were left behind as the three emerged onto a long dim country road. No one spoke as they puffed their way along, then at long last, when

Janie began to think they would be walking all night, the built-up pavement of a village loomed into sight. "Won't be long now," Aunt Pam stated, as they started to climb a short hilly street. Several people were bound in the same direction and Janie guessed they were going to the same meeting. At the top of the hill, bright lights shone out from the open door of a small one-storey building, while the strains of a church organ filled the air. As they paused in front of the entrance, while Aunt Pam vigorously shook the water from her umbrella, Janie glanced up at a small notice-board placed at the side of the doorway and read "Christian Spiritualist Church of" – then a dig in her ribs distracted her and she turned to find John also reading the words. He looked at her and frowned; he seemed anything but pleased. She couldn't understand why, but before she could say anything, Aunt Pam had closed her umbrella and was marshalling them forward.

They were met in the foyer by several people who greeted them and made them welcome. They were shown where to hang their wet outer garments, and then ushered to seats in the main building. Aunt Pam bent her head in silent prayer and Janie and John followed suit. After a few moments the three sat back in their chairs to survey the scene. It was a square pleasant room, brightly lit with two rows of pendent lamps, on this dull wet evening. At one end facing the congregation was a rostrum in the centre of which stood a table covered with an embroidered lace cloth on which was placed a large brass cross, while on either side stood ornamental brass vases filled with multi-coloured roses. There were also water and glasses ready for the speakers' refreshment. To one side was a reading table on which was placed a large bible. At the back of the rostrum were four carver chairs, the seats and backs upholstered in colourful tapestry. A colourful window depicting Jesus healing the sick took central position in the wall facing the rows of people. On all of the window-sills around the hall were vases of flowers; Janie thought she had never seen a more colourful cheerful scene. Even John seemed impressed as he looked around. Aunt Pam glanced at the young couple and a smile of satisfaction crossed her lips.

A man and a woman stepped onto the rostrum from a door at the side, and sat down in chairs each side of the table. The organ stopped playing, while a hush fell over the congregation. The woman rose to her feet and with a smile welcomed the would-be worshippers to the evening service. Then she introduced the man at her side as "Mr. Williams whom I know most of you have met before and we are extremely glad to have with us again." Mr. Williams bowed his head in acknowledgment, after which the service commenced.

Janie thoroughly enjoyed herself. The hymn singing was bright and cheerful and who can sing better than the Welsh? And she joined in with all the gusto of her sweet soprano voice. Mr. Williams gave the address. He spoke seriously, sincerely and with a quiet purpose that seemed to enthrall his audience. He spoke of the work and teachings of Jesus and how His death proved to us that life goes on beyond the grave. He was seen by His friends many times after His death. Had He not said, during his lifetime that "Where I go, there you will go also." Is it not reasonable to expect that there is another world – a Spirit World – where the soul dwells after leaving the physical body? It is a world where all our dreams and aspirations come true. Where we all meet once again with those we love, where life can be very pleasant and happy, if only we have earned it.

Janie's heart throbbed as she listened. Memory stirred, and as her tears threatened to choke her, she was a little girl again and her beloved Grandad stood at her side, talking to her in the same way that Mr. Williams was talking to his congregation. He had said that she should be brought into contact with someone who could explain to her the meaning of her strange experiences. It was as if he knew even then, that as she grew older, her 'strange experiences' would increase.

As she gazed at the speaker on the rostrum, she wondered if at last she had met the one who would open the door to the understanding of the strange and mysterious.

At the conclusion of the service the speaker thanked his congregation for their rapt attention and hoped that someone amongst them had been helped in their search for Truth. He bade those "Goodnight" who had to take their departure and promised after a short rest, to rejoin those who were staying on for the 'communication'.

Janie looked askance at Aunt Pam who was busy gathering her belongings together; she hadn't a clue as to what it was all about, but oh, how she hoped that Aunt Pem would say they should stay. John, on the other hand, seemed a bit fidgety, and anxious to be gone. "I suppose we'd better get on the road," he said, "best be on home-ground when it gets really dark."

"Home-ground?" Aunt Pam snorted, "Anybody would think we were in darkest Africa; we'll go and get a cup of tea and see how many people are staying and also, see what the weather's doing now." On their way to the refreshment room John managed to whisper to his wife that "enough was enough and I am dying for a cigarette." His expression lightened when they entered the refreshment-room. Tea and cakes were being served at a long table and little groups of people stood about laughing and talking – it was a gay, happy scene. After his tea and cake, he took himself off with some other men to smoke a cigarette in a foyer at the back of the building.

Aunt Pam introduced her niece to several groups of people and Janie found them a jolly, friendly crowd. The rain was slowing up and Aunt Pam announced that if they stayed on for the second half of the meeting it would stop altogether for the homeward journey. For some reason Janie was overjoyed; she could have hugged her organising aunt.

In a little while the men rejoined the ladies and those who were staying on made for a smallish room leading off the refreshment room. Here, about twenty chairs were placed in a circle; Aunt Pam sat down and motioned Janie and John to seats either side of her. A hush fell on the assembly as Mr. Williams entered the room and drew a chair up to join the circle. After a hymn and a short prayer, again silence fell, and Janie glancing around noticed that most of the sitters, including Mr. Williams, sat with closed eyes.

Suddenly, the leader opened his eyes and stared round at his mixed audience. To Janie's embarrassment, he focused his gaze on her. After a moment he spoke, his voice soft and dreamy, "At your side is an elderly gentleman, he tells me he is your maternal grandfather and his name is Benjamin. He has led your footsteps here this evening because he knew he could make contact with you. He wants you to know that he still remembers the happy times you spent together when you were a little girl; how you walked in the park on a Sunday morning and how he tried to tell you of the Spirit World – but because you were still so young, he called it the dream world beyond the sunset. He wants you to find out more about the Spirit World and life after death; read books that will help you to understand yourself and the spiritual gifts that are latent within you. They will help you to understand, also, the various experiences you have gone through. Your grandfather will guide your footsteps until he can hand you over to a more competent guide and teacher. In the future you will experience many wonderful spiritual happenings. Life will be very difficult at times and there will be a time of great suffering, but you will face them with courage and fortitude - your inner awareness will tell you they are the pathways that lead to truth."

Mr. Williams paused; gazing steadily at the young woman, he noticed the conflict in the young face – bewilderment, amazement and joy, the eyes bright with unshed tears. "You are a stranger to this movement, are you not?" he enquired, "but do you recognise your Grandfather?"

"Yes, oh, yes! But how do you know? You never met him, and he's been dead for more than ten years." "My dear, there is no death except to the physical body; the real person, the soul, passes on to dwell in the Spirit World, a place of higher and quicker vibrations, which cannot be seen by ordinary earth folk unless they are mediums as I am. A medium has the gifts of clairvoyance and clairaudience, which means he or she can see the spirit people and hear their voices when they speak. All that I have told you comes from your Grandfather. He is anxious to help you know these things. Join a spiritualist church such as this one and you will receive help in developing the spiritual gifts that you have. Now I must get on with the service, there are so many waiting to speak."

Janie's mind was in a whirl – so many things she wanted to know, so many questions she wanted to ask. She tried to analyse her own reception of the things Mr. Williams had told her, and to her amazement she realised she had been waiting a long time to hear them – in fact since her Grandfather had passed from her sight. There was a lot for her to learn, many things for her to find out and understand, but she knew in her heart that the night's happenings were pointers that showed her the way her spiritual footsteps should go.

On the way home she tried to question her Aunt, but that lady was unusually reserved in her answers. She stopped dead in the middle of the road when her niece persisted. "Look here, Janie, and you, John. Why I took you there this evening, I don't know – it was just an impulse, I just had to. But I don't want to force you into anything; your beliefs, choice of religion or creeds – call them what you will, must be your own choice and decision, they are nothing to do with me or anyone else." A slight shadow crossed her features, she seemed puzzled. Then hesitantly she stated, "But I may have been used to point the way, I don't know. Anyway, I can tell you that that little church has been a source of great comfort to me since our Frank was killed in the mine; I know I shall meet him again when my time here is finished. Now, we'll say no more about it. If the spirit people want your service they'll find a way of letting you know." "Yes, that's right, Aunt," John broke in, as he saw that Janie was ready with her questions again, "let's forget it and get home; I'm ready for my supper."

CHAPTER 12:

'GOING TO CHURCH'.

Janie never forgot her holiday in the Welsh mining village and the friendly cosiness of Aunt Pam's little church. Each Sunday evening she visualised the tall straight figure sitting silently with closed eyes, fervently hoping that 'our Frank' would send her his message of love, to let her know he had not forgotten his mother.

Janie never forgot her message. She kept it in her mind and went over it again and again, and often she thought of her grandfather and hoped that in some way she would hear of him again.

She never spoke to John of her thoughts; she had tried to once, but he had shown impatience and said that although he had enjoyed the service at the little church, he thought that "these things are best left alone."

Liz, John's sister, had shown great interest, when Janie had told her of the visit to the spiritualist church; she announced she would make inquiries of the "girls in our department." What they didn't know about what was going on around them, wasn't worth bothering about; if there was a spiritualist church anywhere near, they would know. Sure enough, Liz located one "in the town;" they would have to go by tram, but it wouldn't take long, so if Janie could arrange one Sunday evening, she, Liz, would go with her. Janie made her plans. John had acquired a billiard table and some Sunday evenings his elder married brother came to play the game with him. Floss had said she would stay with young John and put him to bed at the appropriate time. John had raised no objection, when his wife told him of her intentions, except to say he thought she was wasting her time.

Janie's excitement was intense, she thought Sunday evening would never arrive. On the tram, Liz recited some of the comments she had encountered, when making her inquiries of her work companions. Some had been serious and had hoped she would find what she was searching for. Others had laughed and had joked that she was fast "going round the bend:" while one had warned that she had better look out in case a homeless 'spirit' followed her home. Janie asked Liz if any of them had ever visited the church, and Liz replied only those who had treated her seriously, and they had enjoyed the services.

When they had arrived at their destination, Janie's heart sank somewhat as she saw the entrance to the church. It was reached by a wide entry at the side of a large three-storied building. A flight of stairs led up to the first floor landing and a notice on a closed door announced 'Christian Spiritualist Church, Please enter'. While the two women hesitated, wondering what they would find on the

other side of the closed door, a group of people climbed the stairs and murmuring "Good evening," one of them opened the door and bade them enter. A
woman stepped forward and gave them a friendly smile and a warm welcome,
which immediately allayed their fears. They were each handed a hymnbook
and shown to two seats about halfway down the room.

Janie sat down and tried to compose herself as she gazed around. It was a
large airy well-lighted room, and the many chairs were almost all occupied. The
people present appeared to be drawn from all sections of the community,
including husband and wife with teenage offspring, men on their own and
women in groups of two, three or four. On their faces was a look of reverence
and of quiet anticipation. The silence was comforting and relaxing. At the end
of the room was the dais with three chairs, the table with the Bible and the plain
brass cross. Vases of flowers were everywhere, and had it not been for the distant throb of the traffic outside, Janie could have closed her eyes and imagined
herself back in the little church in the Welsh mountains.

The service which followed was earnest and sincere. Liz seemed quite impressed. A hymn was sung after the address while the congregation remained seated. Then a woman stepped forward to he front of the rostrum and stood for a
few moments with closed eyes. Then opening them she spoke quietly to her
audience. "For the sake of the strangers among us, I will explain that we call
this part of our service the 'communication demonstration'. Your dear ones are
here from the World of Spirit and those who so desire will send to you their
messages of love and proof of their survival. They send them through me
because I can see them and hear their voices. I am what is known as a medium
– a channel or instrument for the power of the Spirit. Sometimes the messages
are given to me in symbolic form and I interpret them to the best of my ability;
sometimes, I will give you the symbol as perhaps you will understand the meaning yourselves."

She proceeded to go to various people giving names and incidents relating to
their departed loved ones, and at the very last came to Janie. "Your Grandfather is here – he sends his love and asks you to remember his message to you.
Go on searching, the Spirit World will guide your footsteps, they have need of
your services. Also, there is an Albert here, he belongs to the lady at your side;
he says he is your father and he is now getting adapted to his new life. He says
it was a pleasant shock when he woke up to be told he had 'died'; his old pain-
racked body had been left on the earth-plane, he now had a new painfree body,
very like the old body, but young and supple. His new world was beautiful and
there was a lot for him to see and learn. He would not be back on the earth for
anything, but he still remembers those he has left behind and sends his love.
One day, you will all be reunited."

The amazement on Liz's face made Janie smile – she remembered how she
had felt with her first message. On the way home, there was much to talk about;

Liz said she would like to go again, and so for a short while, 'going to Church' on Sunday evening became the pattern for the sisters-in-law. They did not always get a 'message', but the service was inspiring and uplifting.

Then one day, when Janie was doing her shopping, she saw an announcement outside a newsagent's shop advertising a Spiritualist meeting to be held in a room at the local school. She got in touch with Liz and the two decided to go. It turned out to be a talk on Spiritualism, its history and meaning, with its hopes for the future life after death. The speaker was a Presbyterian minister from Yorkshire, who had become a converted Spiritualist; he spoke well and earnestly and told the reasons for his beliefs and knowledge. After the talk, cups of tea were served and Liz and Janie were able to have a chat with the minister and his wife. Janie was greatly impressed with their enthusiasm and apparent sincerity. She also learned that they were negotiating to buy a house near to where she lived, also to find accommodation to open a Spiritualist Church.

In a few months' time, the visits to church had to terminate as Janie was expecting her second child. Young John, now aged seven, was greatly excited at the prospect of a brother or sister, and one morning he told his mother that he dreamt he had seen his baby sister. She had a lot of black hair and very blue eyes. His father joked about it, and hoped it would indeed be a baby sister, but he would be more interested if she were golden-haired like her mother. Janie said nothing, but her gaze was thoughtful as she smiled at her son. Could the little fellow be psychic? – she wondered.

In less than a fortnight the dream came true; young John's sister was a lovely child, with a lot of dark curly hair and the bluest of eyes. She was given the names of 'Angela Rosemary'. Her mother thanked God as she held the baby closely to her; all had gone well and her little daughter was safely hers.

CHAPTER 13:

THE ROSE IN THE COFFIN..

The days that followed were very busy for Janie, but she never forgot the happy Sunday evenings and hoped one day to be able to resume them, at least now and again, when she had got her little daughter into a normal routine.

In due course Janie's new friends were settled in their new home and had also found suitable premises for their Spiritualist Church. Quite a good congregation was attracted, so Mr. and Mrs. Gaunt – the minister and his wife – gave Saturday evening social events in order than everyone should become acquainted.

About this time Janie's brother, Frank, suffered a grievous bereavement when a beloved sixteen year old daughter died. Hilda was the eldest of his family, a tall attractive girl as fair as Janie herself. A fall on her head in early childhood had caused a scarred brain, unfortunately not discovered until months before her death.

Floss was called into service again as baby-sitter and Janie and Liz were able to go to the new Spiritualist Church in their own locality. Time after time different mediums gave Janie a message purporting to come from Hilda. She was worried about her father – his grief was making him ill and there was no need; she was alive and well and could be happy if only her parents could know of her survival after death. Her physical body only had died; it was like an old worn-out overcoat she had discarded; she, her real self, now dwelt in a lovely world – the Spirit World – with loving people who watched over her, while she could visit her old home as often as she liked. If only her parents could master their sorrow and grow calmer, their daughter would be able to make her presence felt by them. Would Janie, please, take the message home? Janie replied she would try, but she privately had misgivings. Her brother was a very matter-of-fact, down-to-earth man and was not likely to take a 'spirit-message' seriously. Janie prayed for guidance and the next Sunday her prayer was answered.

She received her niece's message, but this time the name 'Hilda' was given with the information that her father had put a red rose inside the coffin; if she – Janie – did not take the message she would be sorry to the end of her days. Only he and his daughter knew about it. Janie was excited and felt she must now do something; she decided to tell her husband and to ask his advice. To her surprise John appeared interested and thoughtful; the usual teasing was forgotten. Then he gave his verdict. "Right," he announced, "you are worrying about this, I think it's more serious than we think. We'll go to see Frank tomorrow evening after I come from work and if he thinks we are mad, well, let him; at least your conscience will be clear."

Janie was shocked when she saw her brother. He had lost considerable weight; his face was pale and drawn, pain and sorrow filled his eyes. After the usual comments on family affairs, Janie glanced uneasily at her husband, hoping for a lead from him as to how she should approach her brother. John took the hint and clearing his throat said, "Frank and Rose, Janie has something to say to you, we are both hoping it will help you." He looked at his wife and nodded his head.

Janie plunged into the account of how she had become interested in Spiritualism and of the meetings and services and the messages that came through the mediums who were the channels of communication between the so-called 'dead' and their loved ones still on earth. She told of the different mediums who had given her indications that Hilda was sending her messages, and that she saw her father put a red rose inside her coffin on the morning of her funeral. Also, she knew his grief for her loss was making him think of doing something that would be both wrong and regrettable. It would not help matters at all.

There was a strained silence as Janie paused in her narrative; she was trembling with nervous tension, her face was flushed, while her hands were hot and dry. Her eyes were downcast – she could not look at her brother and sister-in-law – she prayed that their comments would be kind. Then the sound of broken sobs filled the room. Startled, Janie raised her eyes and saw Frank leaning forward in his chair, his head in his hand, his shoulders shaking with uncontrollable grief. His wife looked helplssly on, bewilderment and pity shadowed her face, until the tears gathered in her eyes and flowed gently down her face. Janie hesitated for a moment, then rising to her feet she ran across to her brother and flung her arms around his crouching form to hold him closely to her.

After a while the sobs ceased and a few moments of calm filled the room. Rose wiped her eyes as she stood up. "I'll go and make a cup of tea," she stated as she glanced uneasily at her husband. Frank stirred, then moving his sister gently from him, he put his hand in his pocket and withdrew a small bottle which he showed to Janie and John. "You are just in time," he said shakily, "Tonight, I was going to take this. You don't know how I miss her and long for her. You know how many doctors and specialists we've taken her to during these past few months or so. But I feel I ought to have realised earlier that she was ill, and done something about it then." He hesitated and then, looking hard at Janie, "I don't understand a bit what you've told me, but I do know that what you've been told is all true and that no-one but me knows anything about it. I'd like to know more of this Spiritualism." Rose came in with the tea and for the rest of the evening, Janie did her best to relate all that she had learnt of the subject and to answer her brother's questions.

They eventually left after Frank told them that he and Rose would visit the new church the following Sunday. Janie was happy and relieved in the knowledge that she had greatly helped her sorrowing brother, and also was instrumental in planting a seed of truth that had been given her from the World of Spirit.

CHAPTER 14:

THE HOME CIRCLE.

Happy times followed. John was quite agreeable to joining the usual social group on Saturday evenings and Rose and Frank joined them. It was there they met Jim and Rita Arnold who had lately come from London and who appeared to know quite a lot about Spiritualism and its implications. They talked of wonderful 'sittings' they had experienced with London mediums and how more satisfying they were than the occasional message from the rostrum. All but John were fascinated; he looked at the Arnolds with distinct suspicion and took refuge in smoking his cigarettes, but his wife and her brother plied the two with endless questions, while Rose looked on with evident interest.

At last Jim Arnold paused to light a cigarette, then keeping his gaze on John, whose suspicion and lack of interest he sensed, he made a proposition to the others. "Look here! There's a lot in this subject that needs looking into; I've no doubt there is a lot of make-believe and blarney. On the other hand, I've experienced things that have set me thinking that it all cannot be false; it's up to us to find the truth; what if we get together and form our own home circle?" He explained what it would entail. They would agree on one evening in the week at the same time, and with no more than eight sitters they would sit in a circle in a subdued light, with soft music from a gramophone. "You can count me out," interposed John defiantly, "I've better things to do with my time; so has Jane, but I expect she will please herself."

Janie looked at him pleadingly, but he would not meet her eyes. She was full of excitement and happy anticipation at the thought of delving into the unknown. In her innermost heart she felt it was not wrong to want to search for things of the Spirit and to find out the secrets of life and death; but her husband refused to discuss it further.

Frank was all for it, while Rose nervously agreed; Janie hesitated, not quite knowing what to do, so Frank, who very much wanted his sister in the circle, suggested that she "come and try it out" and wait and see what the future would bring.

And so, in a fortnight's time, the Circle, that was to bring many friends and happy times, came into being. It was held in the dining-room, at the home of the Arnolds. A thin dark curtain was stretched across one corner of the room and a chair was placed inside for the use of the medium. Mr. Arnold explained that 'the cabinet', the space behind the curtain where the medium sat, was the place where the 'spirit operators' worked after collecting ectoplasm from the bodies of the sitters and especially that of the medium, mixing it in their own

way with chemicals which they brought from the Spirit World. With the substance thus perfected, they would be able to show themselves, speak with their
own voices and their touch would be felt by those in the room. Ectoplasm was
a substance made up of chemicals from the physical body, but its exact make-up
had so far puzzled the scientists.

A good deal of patience was needed as the phenomenon was hard to develop,
so many things had to be taken into account. Each week, the minds and emo-
tions, also the health, of the sitters changed, sometimes for the worse, sometimes for the better, and so the Spirit Operators had to work accordingly, but
it was extremely important that the sitters should sit in harmony one with the
other. They could sing with the music or converse with one another, providing
nothing of a controversial nature was discussed.

Mr. Arnold took the chair in the 'cabinet' until such a time came when the
true medium of the circle would be told them. They opened and closed with a
hymn and a prayer, always praying that God would help them and send someone to them who would guide them and show them how to go on. They sat for
an hour and afterwards, over tea and refreshments, would talk over the evening's events.

Janie went several times and greatly enjoyed the experience; she eagerly
looked forward to it each week, but after a while John grew awkward about her
going; he said he could not see where or how it would all end, and then some
weeks Floss or Liz were not able to baby-sit, and as John was not agreeable to
looking after the children, Janie had to stay at home.

Then one week Mr. Arnold asked Frank if Janie intended coming again to
the circle, as if not, he would have to fill her place. Frank, anxious for his sister's
return, said he would see what he could do, so the following Monday evening
found him at Janie's home. After discussing various topics, he veered the conversation around to the circle. He explained that Mr. Arnold had just purch-
ased a new automatic record player and they needed someone who understood
them and wasn't too interested in the circle to manipulate it in the dark; would
John oblige for a while until they found someone else? He need not take part
in the proceedings, so he could sit just outside the circle. Janie looked eagerly
at her husband, but her heart sank as she noted his vexed, stubborn expression.
"No, I'm not keen! I'd rather you found someone else, I'm not all that
interested."

Frank was not daunted; he glanced at the clock, then got to his feet. "Oh, is
that the time? I must go. Well, think it over, you know it's Friday evening at
7.30. Janie knows the address, if you change your mind – we shall be very grateful." So saying he took his departure; Janie saw him to the front door and he
took her hands and pressed them warmly, winking at her knowingly. Somehow
her spirits rose and she felt hopeful, but on her return John was muttering about
the cheek of people assuming they could tell other people what to do and how

to spend their time.

The subject of the circle; was not broached again; Janie knew how far she could go in arguing with John, but when Friday came and the day wore on, she suddenly felt hopeful and not a little excited. She made sure he had a clean 'best' shirt, while she gave his 'best' suit a good brushing.

Half an hour before his usual time, John arrived home. His expression was half annoyance, half sheepish as he noted his wife's enquiring gaze. "Well! If we're going there tonight I've got to have time to get 'dolled up', haven't I?" he announced. "I'll get your meal," said Janie quietly, but she walked on air to the kitchen.

They arrived on time at the Arnolds' and Jim Arnold seemed delighted to see them. A corner of the room had been prepared for the sitters and while they waited for all of them to arrive, Jim showed off his new automatic radiogram to a very interested John.

Frank arrived with his wife and his eyes glowed as he looked at his sister. John was introduced to the rest of the company, then while they sat in their usual chairs, he sat in one just outside the circle next to the gramophone. The bright lights were switched off and a table lamp with a red bulb took their place. Jim opened with a prayer after which a hymn, 'Open My Eyes', was sung. Then the company settled down to an hour of talking quietly or singing to the music that John played, the table-lamp being switched off. As the hour wore on, Janie felt a happy sense of peace and calm creep over her; she felt the company was good and she sighed contentedly.

As each week came and went, John made no mention of giving up his part in the circle while nothing was said about getting someone else to look after the radiogram. He came home each Friday half an hour early and made up for it at work on another evening. Floss made arrangements to 'babysit' regularly on that evening, so everything turned out well.

Then one evening, Jim told his friends that a young medium from London was coming to stay for a week with him and Rita and that on the next circle night they would be given a 'sitting'. This would entail 'direct voice', a phenomenon whereby the friends from the Spirit World would speak themselves, independently of the medium. Janie could not contain herself, she thought Friday evening would never come. John said little about it, but there was an air of excitement about him.

At last the evening arrived and on the way to the Arnolds', John advised his wife to keep her wits about her at the 'sitting' and to use her eyes and ears to detect if any 'funny business' should be going on, and he would do the same. 'They' would have to be very clever to pull the wool over his eyes, he stated firmly.

When they were all assembled, Jim went out of the room to return with a young man about Janie's age. He was of medium height and build with dark hair and a pleasant countenance. Jim introduced him as Mr. Leslie Flint; he bowed smilingly to the assembled company, but no names were given to him, which, Janie found out in her future dealings with mediums, was the usual custom. Mr. Flint took his seat inside the cabinet with the curtains undrawn; the rest of the company, eight in all, sat in the usual circle with the added presence of Jim and John. Jim opened with a prayer and the hymn was sung, then John reached over to start the records while the light was put out.

For about five minutes there was silence except for the soft music; then suddenly, a boy's cockney voice rang out, greeting the assembled company and especially singling out Jim and Rita Arnold whom he appeared to know. "Hello Mickey," Jim responded, "nice to hear you again, these sitters are members of my home circle and my friends. None of them have ever experienced a 'seance' like this before, so would you please explain who you are and what is likely to happen."

"Yes, mate! You see, ladies and gentlemen, it's like this. A few years ago I lived on Earth; I was a newspaper boy selling papers in the East End of London. I was about twelve and one evening I was run over and killed. Of course I 'ave grown up in the Spirit World – I would be about twenty-seven years old in your world and I have been educated and speak proper, but I chose to come back as I was when I passed over, it's easier for me to communicate and help Leslie in his work. The scientists back 'ere make voice-boxes out of ectoplasm drawn from the medium – that's Leslie, of course; it's all very complicated and you wouldn't understand if I tried to explain. So I think we'd better get on as there's the usual crowd waiting to communicate, and we mustn't waste the power. Now there's a lady 'ere who wants to speak to a John and Jane; she's never communicated before, so John and Jane if you are 'ere, speak up and let the lady 'ear your voice as it will 'elp 'ers to grow stronger."

Janie's head spun, her breath quickened, and she thought her heart would leap from her body. She tried to speak but her voice could not co-operate. Then to her great relief, John at her side spoke out; true, his voice trembled with emotion, but at least he could be heard.

"Hello, my friend! Who are you? I am John and this is Jane, my wife."

"I know! Billy, my little Billy, my boy! Don't you know your mother?" The voice was low, but clear and sweet. Janie looked in it's direction and to her amazement saw the whitish outlines of a woman's form, leaning over what must have been John sitting in the chair next to her.

"Is it really you, Mom? Are you still living – and have you come back to tell me so?"

"It is true, my boy, wonderfully true, and God has led me to the power than has opened the door between the two worlds. Can you understand how I feel, how, ever since I came to the Spirit World, I have sought means to find a way of letting you know that I still live on."

"Oh, Mother, if only we had known; why is it these things are only for the few to know of? If it hadn't been for Jane we would never have met like this, I just can't believe it's true."

"The truth is always elusive and hard to find, but it's worth all the gold and precious gems of your world. Your wife has been inspired and guided ever since she took an interest in life after death. We had to be patient and wait for events to work out our way and at last we were able to bring you to meet Mr. Arnold. I am so glad you have become members of a home-circle – we, on our side, will do all we can to help you. It will take perseverance and a lot of patience, but oh, the joy on both sides when the first 'Spirit Voice' is heard."

"Jane," the voice turned in Janie's direction and she was aware of a form pressing at her side, "how are you, my dear? It isn't every girl who meets her mother-in-law for the first time like this, is it?"

"Oh, I'm quite well, thank you – mother," Janie hesitated over the endearing title, it was all so strange and excited and yet also, so natural. A gentle laugh answered her shyness. "Thank you for calling me 'mother', my dear, I do hope you will not forget me and that we shall have more opportunities to have these little talks."

The 'voice' turned to John and enquired after her daughters Floss and Liz and sent them her love and to tell them that their father would try to communicate at the next opportunity. Then after discussing with both of them, her grand-children, John and Angela, and telling them how she had watched over them since they had been born, she took her leave.

It was wonderful proof for the first time of communicating and Janie and John were congratulated by Mr. Flint and Mr. Arnold on their ability to keep the talk flowing. After the meeting when they were all sat drinking tea, Janie asked her husband why his mother had called him 'Billy'. John laughed and explained to the company that it was his greatest proof that it was indeed his mother.

When he was born he was not expected to live and the local minister was sent for to baptise the baby. He was given the name 'William'. But he thrived and when he was nearly six months old another baptism was carried out in the Church and he was given the names 'John Henry'. But his mother never forgot the weak little baby who fought and struggled to live and she always called him her little 'Billy'.

CHAPTER 15:

GLIMPSES OF TRUTH.

Life went on quite pleasantly for Janie, busy with her children, making their clothes, also her own, and at times for Liz and Floss and Mom. Since her marriage she had become very close to her mother, who made a point of visiting her daughter once a week and spending the day with her. They very often talked of Spiritualism and Janie was pleasantly surprised at her mother's interest. Once, she announced she suspected that "Your Grandfather was a Spiritualist, except that he called it 'The True Philosophy.'" At these words Janie searched her memory to recall the gentle dreamy man who enlightened her childhood with his wonderful accounts of a 'dream-world beyond the sunset'. She wondered how he was faring in that dream-world and if, perhaps, someday he would come back to tell her.

A wonderful rapport had grown between mother and daughter and Janie so often saw her grandfather in the way that her mother spoke and looked with that dreamy far-away expression. She surmised that they were father and daughter for a purpose. Very often Janie and her mother would practise thought-transference and if at any time Mrs. Pullen wished to change the day on which she visited her daughter, she would sit quietly and send out her thoughts to Janie who would pick them up and act accordingly.

Then, one day, Mr. Arnold called in to see John to ask him if in a couple of days' time he could get about two hours off in the afternoon to go to a sitting with a materialisation medium. It was a very rare occasion as the medium, Helen Duncan, had to travel from Glasgow, and the Midlands was not often in her bookings. Jim thought it was an opportunity they should not miss. John said he could manage it by working over, so Janie asked a willing neighbour to have the baby for the afternoon and to take in young John when he came from school which was fortunately only across the road.

The four of them – Rita with her husband – arrived at the house where the sitting was to be held. There were about twenty sitters in all, and they all crowded into a large front room, with a bay-window which had been blacked out with heavy dark curtains. The chairs were placed in two semi-circles facing a corner of the room which was covered by a thin black curtain suspended from a thin wooden rod, the two ends fastened and resting on the picture-rail of two opposite walls. Mr. Arnold walked up to the curtain and, moving it aside, examined the walls and floor, also the plain wooden kitchen chair, the only furniture inside the aperture. He called John and together they made quite certain there was no hidden door or appliance which could be used in trickery. Except for the chair, the space was completely empty. Just outside the curtain, suspended from the ceiling, was a flex holding a small red lamp.

The two men were quite satisfied with their examination and returned to their seats in the middle of the front row. Within a few moments a middle-aged woman entered the room, and introducing herself as "Mrs. Evans" aked for two ladies to go to another room to be present with Mrs. Duncan while she undressed to don the single black garment she habitually wore for her seances. Jim spoke up quickly, "Yes! My wife will go for one." So saying he put her hand under his wife's elbow and helped the surprised Rita to her feet. Another lady in the back row also volunteered, and the two went with Mrs. Evans.

Within a few minutes the two returned, accompanied by a rather stout woman dressed in a black loose dress and a tallish thin woman dressed in a smart blue suit. Without a word to the company, the medium Mrs. Duncan entered the space behind the curtain and sat down on the chair. The other woman stood in front of the sitters and introduced herself as "Mrs. Hamilton". She then proceeded to give some necessary instructions.

The light would be put out and the low red light switched on. A hymn would be sung and the Lord's Prayer said, after which Mrs. Duncan would be in deep trance and 'Albert', her Guide and helper from the Spirit World, would materialise to take control of the proceedings. People were not to leave their seats unless called out to the front and definitely must not touch any materialisation, unless invited to do so. When they were spoken to, they must keep up the conversation, so as to 'hold' the spirit for who was speaking. The spirit communicating would materialise with the ectoplasm from the medium's body, an operation to take place within the 'cabinet' (the space behind the curtain) then he would walk out to find the person he wished to talk to.

An air of excitement and anticipation filled the room as the speaker took her seat next to the cabinet. She turned the pages of a hymn-book and gave out the number, 'Open my Eyes, that I may see, Glimpses of truth Thou hast for me,' a favourite Spiritualist hymn. Before the prayer, she switched on the red lamp, going to the door (which had already been locked, Jim having the key in his pocket) to turn out the overhead white light.

After the prayer, the company coughed and settled itself, then sat quietly with an air of expectancy, while Mrs. Hamilton sang a popular pleasing song, several of the sitters joining in. Then, suddenly, the curtains were drawn apart, and a tall slim, white figure stood in front of the people. There were several gasps of surprise and wonder, and Janie, unable to contain herself, caught hold of Jim's arm and held it tightly. She was aware of John, sitting on the other side of his wife, sitting very tensely in his chair.

The figure spoke in a very cultured voice and gave his name as "Albert". He said there were good vibrations coming from the sitters and they helped the medium enormously; she was giving out excellent ectoplasm, which the spirit operators were able to use to make a first rate sitting. He disappeared inside the curtains again, and thereafter began a steady flow of white clad figures, whose names were given out by the cultured voice, and the sitters in question, calling on their loved ones to engage them in conversation. Many were the glad laughs of wonder and astonishment and a few sobs of emotion as spirit hands were clasped by earthly hands and kisses were exchanged.

Then suddenly, Janie heard her name called by Albert, "Jane Bailey, your grandmother, Mary Ann, is here. She wishes to speak to you."

A figure came out of the cabinet and called to Janie to go to her. She hesitated a moment, then without fear she walked towards the figure of her paternal grandmother. She stood in front of her and studied the features with the lined face and rather sunken eyes and toothless mouth. She recognised her immediately, and with a glad welcome she held out her hands to the being from another world.

The hands that clasped hers were firm, but warm and soft. "Oh, Jane, how wonderful it is that you have been priviledged to communicate like this; we always pray that someone belonging to us will be brought into contact with those who enable them to get in touch with us. We long to let our loved ones know that we are alive, well and happy; it is only our poor physical bodies that have died, but our real self, the soul, is young, full of vitality and energetic. We have no pain or weakness. Our world is very beautiful and we can be very happy, if only we strive to make our lives useful in whatever capacity we choose, mainly in helping those on the earth-plane as well as those in the darker spheres of our world. I come back to you as I used to be, so that you will know me. Look, I will give you further proof." So saying, Janie's hands were unclasped, but one finger was held, and thrust into the spirit's mouth, moving around the toothless gums.

"You never remember your Grandmother with teeth, do you, Jane? I lost my own teeth long before you were born, and I never would have dentures." Janie was amazed, she knew this was true, and said so.

After giving her grand-daughter a private message for her father, the spirit form kissed her, wishing her "goodbye", then seemed to slowly shrink and disappear through the floor.

Janie returned to her seat in a whirl of wonder and amazement. After a while, John's father appeared and talked to his son about intimate family matters; before taking his leave, he bent forward and kissed his daughter-in-law warmly on her lips. As he slowly sank into the floor, his son called, "Dad, I'll tell Liz and Floss I have seen you," but the spirit sadly shook his head. "They'll never believe you, son," he said.

After a while, Albert appeared and said the meeting would have to close as the 'power' was failing and the ectoplasm must be returned to the medium's body. While this was taking place, a hymn was sung and a man gave the closing prayer, during which Mrs. Hamilton helped Mrs. Duncan from her chair, slowly led her to the door which she unlocked, and after closing it again, the man finished the prayer and put on the white light.

Very little was spoken on the way home; the wonders of that afternoon filled each one with their own individual thoughts. The fact that they had all seen and embraced and spoken to loved ones whom they thought they had lost for ever and would never see again, gave them a profound humility and joy, which they wished they could share with everyone.

Janie did not understand the message that her grandmother had given her for her father, but she felt rather apprehensive about giving it to him, as he had laughed mockingly when he was told of Janie's and John's interest. Accordingly, the next time they met, Janie gave her parents an account of the seance. Mom was more than interested and asked questions, but Dad sat with that mocking smile on his lips and refused to say anything.

Then Janie came out with her message. The effect was startling to say the least; the smile left his face and he turned white as a sheet. Whatever that message was, it had gone home. He turned away and stood looking out of the window. Janie looked at her mother who gave her a warning glance but Janie felt satisfied for she knew her father understood: He never mocked again.

CHAPTER 16:

THE MODEL RAILWAY.

For several weeks the little group sat and enjoyed the peace and harmony of the circle. John appeared now to be settled and interested; he confided to his wife that many times he had seen small silver lights like stars darting about, ceiling high in the darkness. Janie also had seen them and Jim told them that they were 'spirit lights' and that they – John and Janie – must be developing clairvoyance.

During this time there was talk of war between Britain and Germany and people went about with anxious faces and talked together in huddled groups, but Mr. Neville Chamberlain, the Prime Minister, made his famous visit to Hitler in Munich, and for the time being war was averted.

Jim Arnold was desirous of forming a 'Psychic Research Society' and asked the members of his circle if they would help him. They all agreed, so Jim set about instructing them as to the procedure.

Janie's clairvoyance had grown by leaps and bounds and Jim said he would find it very useful to the work. First they must have premises to work from as Jim also intended to engage well-known mediums from London and elsewhere to give sittings to interested persons.

After several weeks searching and consulting estate agents, Jim obtained the rental of a disused 'scout's hut' which badly needed cleaning and painting. The eight circle members threw themselves wholeheartedly into the various jobs, working most evenings until quite late at night. Janie made the curtains for the windows, while John installed new wiring for the electrical installations.

At last all was finished and the new 'Psychic Research Society' was duly opened and launched. They were all amazed at the response from the public, people were interested and sought help and advice appertaining to psychic matters. They were asked to help with premises alleged to be haunted and very intriguing some of the cases turned out to be.

John wasn't altogether easy about his wife taking part in such work, but Jim assured him that Janie would come to no harm, while Mr. and Mrs. Gaunt kindly helped them with their expert advice. Eventually, the premises of the 'Psychic Research Society' in York Road was mistaken for a Spiritualist church and people used to turn up for the Sunday services. Jim had to explain their error and direct them to Mr. Gaunt's church.

But all this set Jim to thinking and he decided that Kings Heath could do with two churches. He talked it over with the rest of his Circle, but Janie and John were dead against it, as they thought they might interfere with the Gaunts' congregation and they had worked so hard to get their church started. Jim told them that his church would be slightly different as he intended to apply for membership of the 'Spiritualists' National Union', a body which incorporated all religions, while Mr. Gaunt's church was a 'Christian Spiritualist' church.

Janie talked it over with Mr. and Mrs. Gaunt and both reassured her that Kings Heath was large enough for two churches, so Jim went along with his plans.

The Circle carried on as usual and Janie still looked forward to Circle Night with excitement and anticipation, feeling that each week something inside her was slowly changing, giving her an awareness that Spirit was indeed very close.

At this time, John was busy building a model railway around the walls of his son's bedroom; young John was 'mad' on railways, and would spend all the time he could spare on the station of a nearby rail line. He had been collecting model equipment for some time in the form of birthday and Christmas presents from generous aunts and uncles, also saving his own pocket money to buy the precious pieces.

At last all was ready, and amid great excitement young John pulled the switch that set the engine in motion, gliding swiftly and smoothly around the bedroom walls pulling the passenger coaches with it. The young lad could not thank his father enough, he was old enough to know that he had made an expert job of a model railway with the yards of track, signals and station, complete with railway staff and lighting equipment.

One night, when her son had been in bed for a couple of hours, Janie had reason to go upstairs and passing the boy's bedroom heard the sound of the engine and coaches running around the track. Angry that the youngster should be playing at that late hour instead of sleeping, she burst into the room; to her amazement it was in darkness. Her hand searched for the light switch and as the light came on, the railway came to a sudden halt, the engine and coaches toppling over. Young John was in bed fast asleep. Also, the ornaments and his personal things were in disarray on the dressing-table, in fact the room was decidedly untidy.

Janie just could not believe it, nor could she explain it. Just then she heard her husband's footstep on the stairs, she tiptoed out onto the landing and in a whisper told him what had happened. He looked at her unbelievingly, then, stepping into the room, he looked round it thoroughly, making sure that his son was indeed fast asleep. Then he turned out the light and quietly left the room, closing the door after him.

Janie, bewildered, questioned him, but he put a finger to his lips while he murmured, "Let's see what happens." They both stood close to the door, listing for any sound from within. Suddenly, the railway came to life, the wheels of the engine and coaches turning smoothly, while from the direction of the dressing-table came sounds that told them that things were being sorted out there.

Then there was silence and after a few moments, John decided there would be no more activity; he quietly opened the door and put on the light. Everything was in order, the room tidy and young John still fast asleep. After looking critically around, John smiled knowingly at his wife, while he drew her gently from the room.

CHAPTER 17:

JANIE'S GREATEST PROOF.

About this time war clouds gathered across Europe causing a great deal of talk and some anxiety, but Janie, ever optimistic, could never think of such a thing happening. Her main concern was the bringing up of her two children and looking after her husband and home. Also the Circle had come to mean such a lot to her and John. Except for one change they were still the same seven friends who had started and they all appeared to get on well with each other, which was most important, as harmony was most essential in the success of such a Circle.

Jim Arnold was still the leader or medium, and every week at the end of the sitting, his Spiritual Guide, Great White Cloud, would enter him and speak to them on very profound and interesting matters, giving them advice appertaining to the running of the Circle. He sounded a very gentle, wise soul. When on the earth-plane he had been a North American Indian, but it seemed he had been in the Spirit World a great many years.

Janie always felt a wonderful sense of peace and tranquillity, and of late she had seen flashes of silver light dart across the darkness. She told John, and it seemed that he also had seen them. They both seemed to be developing their own psychic gifts, and when they sat quietly with closed eyes they would see various pictures in colour form. Jim was very pleased when they told him, and said they were developing clairvoyance. After a very short while Janie could make sense of the pictures she saw. This fact made Jim thoughtful. He sensed that Janie was more and more aware of her mediumistic powers. The aim of the Circle was to develop physical phenomena, which means that the Spirit entities could materialise by means of ectoplasm and speak in their own voices.

Then it happened: war was declared, and for a while people were stunned. Then instructions from the Government were issued and everyone sprang into action, buying black material to make up into curtains for every window, as it was an offence to allow light to shine through at night time. Also, the men were busy erecting the air-raid shelters issued by the Goverment. During the day-time women were besieging the shops to buy what food they could, to keep in store against shortages. Janie thought that was all very well, but you needed money for that sort of thing, and Janie and John had very little put by. However, Janie, still as optimist as ever, decided that God would provide, as it seemed He always had done.

John went to town in his efforts with the shelter. He was determined to make it as comfortable as he could, for he suspected that a great deal of time would be spent down there, at least for his wife and children. He made a wooden floor and covered it with a mattress his sister had given him. Then he set to work to make two bunk beds for the children; he also wired for an electric light and a power point for an electric fire. The fire was installed on it's own shelf high up out of reach of the children.

When Janie and John between them had done everything they could with the war preparations, they realised all they could do now was to wait for further developments. Janie went, as usual, on her Monday evening visit to see her mother, taking baby Angela with her. Recently Mom and Dad had been to South Wales to Dad's twin brother's funeral, and both of them had caught a bad cold. It had been a bitterly cold windy day in mid March, and the slow walk to the churchyard, which was situated on the lower incline of a mountain, had proved too much for them. Janie was shocked when she saw her mother; she had a nasty wheezy cough, she breathed with difficulty, while she appeared to have lost weight. "Oh, Mom," she cried, "You seem very poorly, you ought to see a doctor." "Oh, I'm alright, it's just a cold caught walking to that churchyard; I wonder why they don't drive to it, like they do here. I'm taking some cough mixture, I'll be alright, I don't need a doctor; but your Dad worries me, he's been very quiet since we got back from Wales. I think he's shocked by your Uncle's death; we were just half an hour too late to see him." "Poor Dad," answered her daughter, "you seem to have struck a bad patch, you must both of you look after yourselves."

Poor Mom! The preparations for war had been getting her down. She had been through one ghastly experience between 1914 and 1919, and almost lost two sons. When she went to collect her gas-mask, she had fainted right away when it was fitted on her; and Dad had flatly refused to install the air-raid shelter, saying that no Hitler would run him down to earth.

Jane went home in a very thoughful mood and told John of her concern. He advised that she should not leave it a week before paying another visit and to take some lemons with her to make her mother a hot lemon drink; but before then, Frank called to see them on his new motor cycle to tell them Mom was very poorly and Dad had suffered a severe haemorrhage and was also in bed. He – Frank, had gone for the doctor, who had promised to see the sick couple after his surgery, and he had left a neighbour in charge while he came to fetch Janie. The baby was already in bed and as young John was capable of putting himself to bed, and her husband would be there to look after him, Janie put on her coat and perched on the pillion seat of the motor-cycle; they were soon at the family home.

Mom had a very heightened colour which Janie did not like, also her breathing was very laboured. Poor Dad on the other hand, was as white as a sheet and he seemed very weak and weary. The doctor arrived before she could say anything and, after giving Janie a brief nod, he proceeded to examine her parents. After he had finished he turned to Janie, his face very stern. "Call your brother, will you, he should be here." Janie hurried to the head of the stairs and called out for Frank. "Your parents are both very poorly," the doctor told them, "they need treatment that I cannot give them at home. They must go to hospital."

"No, no!" Dad cried in a shaky voice, "I'm not going to hospital, I shall be alright, I've got to get to work."

"Then, if you won't go," said Mom, "neither will I, so you go to work and I'll stay here," and Mom ended her statement in a fit of harsh coughing. Frank and Janie stared helplessly at the stubborn couple, so the doctor sat on the edge of the bed, and reasoned with them. He told them their attitude on each side was interfering with the other's urgent treatment, that Mom's breathing could get worse and Dad could have another haemorrhage.

Dad looked at Mom and a worried frown passed over his face. "Alright, have it your way, but only for a few days, mind."

Janie went in the ambulance with her parents, while Frank followed on his motorbike; they both saw the sick pair installed safely in their beds, the staff kindly putting them in separate rooms very near to one another in the same corridor. The next evening Janie went in with her sister, Jessie, to visit their parents, and while Jessie expressed her satisfaction at her mother's improved condition, Janie gazed at her with some apprehension. She was propped up in bed and seemed quite lively and talkative, but, Janie did not like the flush in her cheeks, which seemed more purple than rosy. They stayed with her for a time then popped down the corridor to see Dad; he was very pleased to see them and inquired after Mom. Jessie interposed to state that she thought her mother was a lot better and seemed very happy and she thought that Dad appeared to be the same. Janie hung back a little; she had not intention of alarming her father with her misgivings; maybe she was being a little fanciful.

Next morning, after her husband had left for work and young John for school, Janie asked her neighbour to have little Angela while she ran to the phone kiosk to phone the hospital for news of her parents. She got through to her mother's ward and the voice at the other end inquired her identity. "Oh, please hold on, sister wishes to speak to you." An icy hand took hold of her heart, while her legs shook so much she could hardly stand. At last, Sister's voice came through. "I am very sorry, Mrs. Bailey, but your mother passed away at eight o'clock this morning, she went very peacefully." Janie rebelled aganst the news, she could not believe it; Mom would never do that, go without a word or a goodbye.

"No, no," she cried, "You've made a mistake, you've got the wrong patient; oh, God don't let it be true ...... Frank, I must find Frank, he'll know."

Janie dropped the receiver and let it swing. Sister's voice was still coming through; she pushed open the door and ran madly up the quiet road, straight into the arms of her brother. Frank held her close, murmuring, "I just missed you, I tried to get here before you went to the phone, there.... there, don't take on so, these things have to be faced." And he shook his sister firmly as her dry sobs made her breathing difficult. Frank led her home and put on the kettle while Janie sat on the sofa and sobbed quietly to herself. He brought her the tea and sat down besides her. They sipped their tea in silence, then Frank put down his cup and turned to his sister, "I was with Mom when she...she," he paused awkwardly, "went... She had had a good night and just before eight she woke up and said she had been to a wonderful place and she was going back to it, she had just slipped back to give us all her love and to say goodbye ...... she said to tell you that when she can, she will get in touch."

Janie stared wide-eyed at her brother, then as the words sank in a flush of excitement touched her cheeks. "Oh, thank God," she breathed. "I knew there would be something from her." "But poor Dad, he'll be so upset, he won't understand," Frank broke in. "There's another thing; the doctors say we must not tell Dad yet about Mom as the shock will bring on another haemorrhage, and he won't be able to stand another one, so we've all got to be very careful."

The next day was Saturday, and over the weekend, Dad had more than his fair share of visitors. Janie did not go then as she stood back for the workers who could not visit in the week; Jessie, being one of these, was among half a dozen or so friends who stood about the bed on Sunday afternoon when two doctors arrived to see their patient. Dad was extremely tired and the doctors were very annoyed. They immediately cancelled all visiting until further notice. As Janie had arranged to see her father on Monday afternoon, Jessie hurried from the hospital to tell her sister she must not go. Janie was both upset and annoyed; why didn't people use their common sense? Two at a time could have gone in and stayed for a short time, the others waiting in the corridor. Now poor Dad would have no visitors, and she wouldn't know how he really was.

She worried about it all the rest of the Sunday, and on Monday morning after her husband and young John had left the house, she sat down with a cup of tea and gave the matter some thought. Suddenly, a vision of Dad's white drawn face appeared in front of her, and it seemed he was imploring her to do something. There was no doubt about it, he was thinking of her and he needed her. Quickly she rose to her feet and put on her outdoor clothes; then running into the garden to look at baby asleep in her pram, she hurried next door to ask her neighbour to keep an eye on the baby for her.

She arrived at the hospital about eleven o'clock and knocked rather hesitantly on Sister's door; after all, they might not let her see her father. A voice called out, "Come in," Janie duly obliged and found Sister sitting at a desk writing. She put down her pen and looked round at her visitor, who stated her requirements. Sister looked searchingly at the young woman; "Are you Janie? I can see that you are the fair one; your father has been asking for you all morning. We were going to send for you after lunch."

"Dad isn't worse, is he?" asked Janie, rather alarmed.

"No, he's about the same, but we didn't want him to worry and he seems rather anxious to see you."

Janie thanked Sister and went on to Dad's room. His face lit up as she bent to kiss him, then, drawing up a chair, she took his hand. "Now, Dad, what is bothering you? I knw you wanted to see me, that's why I came."

A look of delight spread over his face. "Janie," he stated in a weak but clear voice, "Your mother came to see me yesterday morning."

Startled, Janie just stared at him, then pulling herself together, she asked quickly, "You mean a nurse brought her in a wheelchair?"

He shook his head impatiently, "No, no; I had turned to look out of the window to see what the weather was like for the visitors, and when I turned around Mother was standing by the bedside."

"What did she look like, Dad?" Janie asked, struggling to choke back her tears, "and did she speak to you?"

"She looked just like she did on our wedding day; and she said, "Don't worry, Bert, I am with you; I flung back the bedclothes and told her, "Jane, I am coming with you, but she stopped me and said, "Not yet. I will come again."" The sick man sighed deeply, "And then she went away."

Janie broke in, "You mean she went away through the door?"

He shook his head. "No, she just sank through the floor."

Janie was at a loss what to say; how could she make her father understand? She knew, of course, that the soul of her mother had communicated with her husband, but remembering his past disbelief and scoffing, would he now believe her if she tried to explain? Also, she would have to tell him his wife had died, so what would the doctors say?

Her father stirred himself, he took his daughter's hand, "You know, girl, I know what Mother means; she wants me to stay for a while with you children to look after you, then she'll come and take me with her." Janie felt her heart was breaking, her tears flowed, unchecked. She bent over and put her arms around the wasted figure on the bed.

"Dad, you are not to worry about us girls, we are all married and have someone to look after us, just think of yourself and.... and Mom."

The light came back to his eyes. "You mean I can go with her when she comes?"

"Dad, I want you to do whatever is right and what will make you happy." Not once had he asked if his wife had died or thought her appearance was unusual; he seemed to know what had happened and how to cope with it.

The door opened and Sister stepped into the room. "Mrs. Bailey," she said, "The doctors have come to see your father, you needn't go, just wait outside."

Janie brushed a hand across her tear-stained face and, getting up from her chair, embraced her father. "I can't stay any longer, Sister, I must get back to the baby." She gave her father one last long look and turned from the room.

Outside, in the corridor stood three men in white coats. She addressed herself to the senior looking one. "My father has been talking about my mother; he knows she has died. No one has told him, she came herself to tell him. It's made him very happy."

The three men looked at each other, then the older one spoke. "I am sure it has, my dear. I understand what you mean."

Janie stared at him, seeing him in a new light, the tears brimming over again. She murmured "Thank you;" and turning on her heel, sped away down the corridor.

Mom's funeral was arranged for Wednesday at twelve noon; Rita Arnold had kindly offered to have little Angela and John took her there, on their way to the funeral. They had been talking a few moments when the telephone rang. Rita answered it; her face grew very grave and troubled as she listened to her caller, then she put down the phone and turned to the young couple, "I'm sorry," she said, "That caller was Frank. Janie, your father passed away this morning, he went very quietly."

Janie shivered and felt the blood drain from her face. So Mom had kept her word and had come back for Dad. She pictured his eagerness and the light in his eyes as he held his arms out to his wife and her tears fell in sympathy with their happiness.

On the slow drive to the cemetery, Janie's mind went back over the years and she remembered the first time she had gone to a Spiritualist meeting with her sister-in-law, and how the two of them had behaved rather badly. They were both cynical and amused and the medium going around the sitters with her messages from the unseen commentators, picked it up. She had come over to the two girls and looked very hard at Janie. "I know this is your first visit to one of our churches," she said, "but it won't be your last, you are searching for something and over the years many wonderful experiences will be given to you. You are amused now because you are doubtful, but someone very close to you, who also laughs at our truths, in the future will give you your greatest proof." Janie sighed, but her heart felt lighter; she knew that past prediction had reached fulfilment in Dad's room at the hospital.

CHAPTER 18:

A CAVALIER BODYGUARD.

As the days went by, Janie missed her parents very much, especially her mother and her visits to her. One evening, John had gone out into his garden, after the evening meal, to have a look at his car which had been giving him trouble. He was leaning over the bonnet, when he felt someone at his side. Glancing round, he saw a very strange figure; he did not know the man and concluded that his strange attire was a sort of fancy dress. He said good evening and asked what he could do for him, but the man did not speak, just stared and half smiled as he moved towards the back of the car. John followed him, but then stopped short, astonished. He was nowhere to be seen! Where could he have got to? There was nowhere he could be hiding. Very puzzled, John went back into the house to see if his wife could enlighten him. Janie was as puzzled as he was, and putting down her sewing, followed him out into the back yard; there was no-one there and concluding it must be a visitor to one of her neighbours who had come to the wrong house, she turned to go back to her sewing and nearly knocked over the man they were looking for. Where on earth could he have come from? The path leading to the road was clearly in view, and he certainly had not come up that, and since John was near the fence leading to the neighbour's garden it was clear that he hadn't climbed over that. Besides, Janie thought, eyeing him up and down, he would have a bit of a job in that getup. His costume was made of silk and satin heavily trimmed with lace, the knickerbockers were cream colour and the jacket a soft rose pink. On his head was a black hat swathed about with an ostrich feather; he gazed at her with piercing dark eyes, and with a start, Janie noticed the long curling hair falling over each shoulder.

"Who are you looking for?" she ventured, then stopped, as the strange figure lifted a hand in her direction and said quietly: "You, Madame," then promptly disappeared into thin air. John, who had witnessed the man's vanishing act, ran over to his wife's side and put his arm about her as he saw her white face and startled, staring eyes.

"What on earth is going on?" he shouted as he led his wife back into the kitchen, she was trembling violently, so he placed her in a chair at the table and put a kettle on the stove to make a comforting 'cuppa'.

He let her sip her tea in silence, then as she grew calmer, he asked, "What did he say to you, why was he here and who is he?" "I only know what he said, I asked him who he was looking for, and he pointed at me and said "You, Madame.", then you must have seen him vanish; I didn't get a chance to say any more."

John looked very thoughtful and he sat quiet for a time. Then, getting to his feet, he put his hand into his pocket and withdrew some coins. "I'll go and give Jim a ring and ask him to come over. He'll know more about all this. I won't be long – but you had better lock the door," he hesitated, looked at his wife and grinned sheepishly. Then, turning, he went on his errand.

John was scarcely back from phoning when Jim and his wife arrived; it had only taken them a few minutes in the car. Clearly, they were both excited. "Now tell me everything that happened and don't leave anything out," Jim said tensely, fixing his gaze on John, who was beginning to feel a bit of a fool; but he plunged into his story and told everything exactly as it had happened.

After her husband had finished, Janie quietly added her version. Jim leaned back in his chair, closed his eyes and was silent. At last he spoke:

"Of course, your strange man must be a materialization, as both of you saw him together, but why he is here and what his purpose is we may find out later on."

"But," broke in John, "Is that possible outside of the circle rooms?"

"Oh yes; there must be a build up of psychic power around here somewhere, but what power – and in the daylight too. I know it was getting dark, but it seems there was sufficient light for you to work on the car. By the way," he added, "Are you still having the disturbances at night in young John's room?"

"Oh yes, now and again, but we've grown quite used to it now and it doesn't bother us at all."

"Mmmmm," Jim stroked his chin and looked very thoughtful, but he did not say anything.

*   *   *

The next time the young couple went to the circle, Jim announced that he had been in touch with his friend, Leslie Flint who had accepted a booking for the Church on the next weekend. Janie was thrilled at the prospect; she knew Leslie was a very gifted medium, for they had sat with him several times and had received wonderful evidence; also, she hoped they would receive some light on the identity of the 'cavalier' as she called him.

At their next circle sitting, Leslie Flint agreed to sit with them, and once again the meeting urned into a wonderful discourse between the two worlds. Mom came through and her ability to communicate was quite evident, for her voice came through loud and clear, which pleased Janie very much; she knew that quite often many of the communicators broke down because they found difficulty in manipulating the spiritual 'voice box'.

After several spirit friends had spoken, Mickey's voice was heard and he sounded a little peeved – Mickey was the boy control who was in charge of the proceedings, keeping the communicators in order, and seeing that they spoke in strict rotation. He was usually rather comical and helped to lighten the vibrations, which is very necessary for this type of phenomena: "There's a bloke here talking a foreign language, he won't tell me who he wants, but he's pushed his way through; can you understand him, Mr. Arnold?"

A voice was heard speaking quickly and rather excitedly, but not in English. Jim listened, but could not make out the words.

"Friend, you are very welcome, but we cannot understand you. Can you speak in English?" There was some indistinct muttering, then a voice came through loud and clear, though with a pronounced French accent.

"I am Leon Lechum, and I lived in France a long time ago. I have been assigned to protect Madame Janie during the coming conflict and I hope I can help you all. You must put your trust in God and in the Spirit World."

"But why specially Janie? And the conflict, do you think things will bad?" Jim sounded anxious.

"Madame Janie has work to do in the future for Spirit, we do not wish harm to come to her. As to hostilities, you have never known the like before. Your cities will be razed to the ground, many will pass over to our side."

Janie felt a cold hand grip her heart, while the rest of the circle were silent with shock. The voice continued, "I am sorry to upset you. Now, I must go, others are waiting to speak."

Janie roused herself and broke in quickly, "Leon, please tell me, are you the cavalier we have been seeing lately, and how are you able to materialise?"

"Yes, Madame, I am your cavalier, and I obtain my power from you."

CHAPTER 19:

THE DARK DAYS BEGIN.

In the days that followed, the circle members went about their work and social life as usual, but they were all much more serious and at times misapprehension darkened their eyes. There were changes in almost every household. Those people who were not eligible for the armed forces, were directed to the government controlled factories, and John, who was a skilled electrician, was directed to a contractor, who would be responsible for getting the factories working after enemy action. In the meantime he was busy with the electrical work on the gun-sites around the outskirts of the town. The days were long and arduous and he arrived home late at night, feeling tired and depressed.

Young John had already been evacuated with the rest of the schoolchildren, and Janie was missing him very much. She was praying that they had made the right decision in sending him away, but her mind was in a whirl with conflicting thoughts. He might be safe from the bombing, but suppose that she and his father and little Angela were killed in an attack, what would happen to him then? Wouldn't he rather take a chance and be with them? She felt he did not like being away from them all, although he did not complain, but sometimes he sent them plaintive little notes through the post which, when Janie read them, filled her heart with misgivings. In the end, she decided to pray about it and see what happened.

Now and again, when John could take a Sunday off from work, they would take a packed lunch and drive over to see their son, who was billeted with a childless couple in a nice house in a country village about twenty five miles from Birmingham. Janie sensed the wife was very houseproud, and she watched young John like a hawk. When it was time for them to leave for home they said goodbye to their hosts and thanked them once again for looking after their son, who followed them outside to the car. There was a strained look on his face; Janie asked what he would do now before his bedtime? "Oh," he replied, "I'll go and play with David who lives down at the bottom of the lane." His mother looked down to where he pointed, then rather anxiously she said, "Well, keep your eye on the time, get back before dark." Somehow she just could not say "home."

Then the lad said a strange thing. "I shall be alright, Mom, the lady will see me home."

"What lady? You mean your friend's mother?"

"No, I mean the lady in white. When I'm a bit late she is waiting for me and she walks with me to the gate, and when I say "Thank you and goodnight," she smiles and goes away."

"You mean she goes back the way you've come?" his father interposed.

"Oh no! She just smiles and then disappears."

"Hasn't she ever spoken to you? Where does she come from and why do you call her "the lady in white"?" asked Janie.

"She always wears a long white dress; her hair is dark and she has very blue eyes. She reminds me of Aunty Lizzie," her son responded.

John was very thoughful on the way home. The lad's description fitted John's mother perfectly, but whoever she was, he was grateful to know she was looking after the boy.

*   *   *

Autumn seemed to fall quickly that year. 1940 was a year of doubt, indecision, apprehension, hard work and no play. Those families with children who had been evacuated were mostly upset with the breakup of their family life. Had they done right in sending the little ones away from home to live among strangers? How did they know they would be safe from the bombing? They had been too quick to assume there would be any bombing at all. Anyway, everyone had an issue of an air-raid shelter, so, surely, if one part of the family would be safe in them, so would the children who had been banished to the country.

Janie knew that most mothers were thinking on those lines; she had almost convinced herself that young John would be better at home; the longing in his eyes when they last said, "Goodbye," just haunted her. She would wait a while longer to see how things developed.

Her birthday, October 1st, dawned and among the birthday cards from relatives and friends was one from her son. The tears flowed as she read the faltering writing in pencil. "Dear Mommy, Happy Birthday, I wish I was home to kiss you. Perhaps one day I shall get home." Janie doubted no longer; it was only right they should all be together. If the bombing did come and they were hit, at least she and her husband could hold the children fast and face together whatever might come.

That night she showed the card to John and asked him if he could possibly get the following Sunday off from work to fetch the youngster home. He read the message very carefully, his face very stern, then, handing back the card, he grunted: "That lad must practise up his writing when he comes home."

Janie's heart brimmed over with relief and happiness, as she set to write the necessary letters to her son and his guardians to acquaint them of their intentions on the following Sunday afternoon.

And when Janie saw the happy excitement on her son's face she knew they were doing right in bringing him home.

Then in a few short weeks the air-raids they had lived in fear of started in grim earnest. One night Janie was awakened by an unfamiliar noise..... Thud, thud, thud... while the house seemed to vibrate. She quickly ran to the window and leaned out; she saw rays of light cutting across the sky and she decided it was a funny type of thunder storm. Fascinated, she watched, until a voice behind her startled her back into the present.

"What in the name of goodness are you doing, how long has this been going on?" enquired John, as he peered out into the darkness.

"Oh, the thunder woke me up. I've never seen such a thunder storm."

"And you are not seeing one now. That's guns being fired, the bombs have started. They seem to be some distance away as yet. Hurry up and get yourself dressed, then wrap up the baby, and I'll see to John." Even as he spoke the alert sounded, sending a cold chill down Janie's spine.

They collected the children, warmly wrapped them up, and hurried down to the shelter; the bunks were snug and comfortable, and soon they were fast asleep again. But their parents sat in silent apprehension, wondering what the night would unfold. By five thirty, when the "All Clear" sounded, the conflict had come very little nearer to them, so many people sighed with relief.

But after that, things grew steadily worse. The bombing started earlier every evening, and by five o'clock the children were tucked up safely in the shelter, while Janie had cooked her husband's meal and put it in the oven to keep hot for when he arrived home about six thirty. Many nights he would sit in the house to eat his meal, then putting on his helmet and wellington boots, would run through the inferno of bursting shells and exploding incendiary bombs to the shelter to see how his wife and children were going on, before joining the other six wardens in putting out the fires on the nearby railway lines.

Then one night Janie had a strange experience. The children were sleeping peacefully, and as she sewed, utter weariness took hold of her, so, making herself comfortable, she too fell fast asleep.

Suddenly, she found herself hurrying through the turmoil outside the shelter. The sound of bombs falling, men shouting, the railway line lit up with the incendiaries' fire, did not deter her as she ran towards the bombed buildings. She felt she had done this many times before, and knew she was safe and could not be harmed. All at once, a misty figure draped in white was at her side, a hand was held out to her, and she took it gratefully. Thereafter, the pair seemed to float just above ground level, and in a trice they were at the scene of their objective.

They seemed to be in a factory area, with houses scattered about. Most of the larger buildings had been bombed and were on fire; fire engines were everywhere, while ambulances were screaming to a halt, and men in tin hats and wellingtons were shouting instructions. Many of the houses, also, were on fire, and it was towards these that Janie and her companion made their way. They entered the burning houses fearlessly, and the cries of little children tore at Janie's heart. But some lay still and lifeless, young babies in the arms of their unconscious mothers; toddlers flung from loving arms, and teenagers, some of them lying across the little ones, as though endeavouring to shield them. Then all at once, there was an army of white robed people who seemed to be doctors and nurses; they were looking at Janie, and one, who appeared to be the leader, smiled at her and nodded encouragingly.

She went up to the first toddler, and gently spoke to it, holding her hands above its head, and in a short time, a replica of the child rose slowly from the top of the head and Janie lifted it tenderly from the broken body and handed it to the nearest helper. So this went on, until all those dazed souls were helped by loving, caring people. The older casualties were able to leave their bodies themselves, but they were also in need of the help at hand.

Janie kept these experiences to herself; she did not wish to be laughed at; she knew that John would say it was all dreaming. She could not explain it, but she knew that it was more than that.

CHAPTER 20:

ESCAPE TO THE COUNTRY.

In view of the nightly bombing, to everyone's regret, the circle was given up, but from time to time, Monsieur Lechum would show himself to give his smile of encouragement and Janie continued her work with her nightly Spiritual companions.

Then one night when things were quiet and the sirens had not sounded, it was John's turn to snatch a few hours sleep in the shelter. His wife was the first to awaken to find that she and her husband were lying in a few inches of water. After days of continuous rain, a portion of the concrete floor had given way, allowing the water through. John found out afterwards that he had built the shelter on a dried up spring, which the heavy rain released. Everything was still quiet, so they decided to finish the remaining hours in the house and leave until morning the clearing up they must do.

It became impossible to use the shelter any more, so each evening, Janie wrapped up the children warmly, and, taking pillows and blankets, went to the nearby horse-shoe tunnel to shelter. It was a deep, wide, airy place and many families sought refuge there from the bombing and for a few nights they were reasonably comfortable and able to sleep a little.

But it did not last. As the bombing grew more intense in the inner city, those who could were driven to seek shelter in the suburbs. Soon, the tunnel became packed with standing people, while only the children and the old were able to sit up against the walls. Janie stood many nights with the restless baby in her arms, propped up tightly with the standing figures around her.

Then one day in November, when the weather was bleak, cold and foggy, young John complained of not feeling well; his throat and neck hurt and his head ached. His mother saw that he had a temperature and she made him stay in bed. She did what she could to ease him, but towards evening he seemed to grow worse and when her husband came in from work, she asked him to fetch the doctor who only lived at the top of the hill.

He announced that the young patient had tonsilitis and must be kept in the warm at all costs as he had a high fever. Janie asked him about going into the shelter when the air-raid was on, but he shook his head. Young John must stay in bed and not be moved. He suggested that his bed should be protected by overlays from the other beds and, since his father had to be on warden duty, someone should take the baby into the shelter, while she stayed with her son. He wrote out a prescription for the boy and returned again to the top of the hill.

That night a kindly neighbour took baby Angela into the tunnel. Young John slept fairly peacefully during the air-raid, due, his mother suspected, to a soothing agent in his medicine, while she spent most of the night lying across his body, as each blast seemed specially directed towards that little bedroom.

When John came home the next night he brought with him his sister who agreed to look after Angela during the air-raids. Young John seemed to be making only slow progress towards recovery; plainly the doctor was worried. He looked closely at Janie one morning when he called in to see his patient. "Haven't you a relative or friend in the country who could put you and the children up for a few days, until the boy is better. You are looking rather ghastly as well. When was the last time you slept?"

Janie gave him a wan smile, but shook her head. "I have a brother who was bombed out; he managed to get a large room in a farmhouse for his family, but we have no one else outside Birmingham."

"Well things have been somewhat quiet these last couple of nights. Do what you can to get some sleep and I'll change the lad's medicine."

Janie told her husband when he came home from work, and he looked very thoughtful. From time to time he ran into his brother-in-law, Frank, who worked near at hand, so he would try to have a word with him. If anyone could help them he was the one. Sure enough, in a few days' time, he came home all excited. A tenant had suddenly left his room at the farmhouse, and Frank had persuaded the farmer to let his sister have the room. Janie hesitated, she did not wish to leave her home, but young John worried her; while she herself was feeling very unwell. Perhaps a couple of weeks in the comparative peace of the country would do her and the children good, and who knows, perhaps by then, the bombing would ease off. She decided to go; she could not explain it, but something seemed to be compelling her to move away. Her husband would have to stay because of his work and warden duties; still, a couple of nights' sleep in the country would do him the world of good, for it seemed ages since he had removed his clothes to sleep a few hours in bed. Whenever he could snatch any time for sleep it was in the armchair – she could not understand how he kept going.

John made arrangements to take his family to the country the following Saturday afternoon, together with the beds, as the farmer had no spare furniture to lend. He went to see the warden in charge before setting out, and came back with the news that he had been given permission to stay overnight.

In view of what happened, Janie marvelled at the way she and her family were protected; for that night saw one of the worst bombing onslaughts. The mouth of the tunnel received a direct hit, and many people were killed, including the six wardens; also, their home was badly damaged and was now unfit for habitation.

Her husband and her brother went the next day to collect what furniture they could from the damaged house, and on their return John saw Mr. Cleavly, the farmer, to ask if they could have the tenancy of the very large bedroom, until they could find somewhere else to live. Mr. Cleavly agreed and suggested that they could share the sitting room with Janie's brother and his family. That evening when they were all together, John told Frank and his wife, Rose, what Mr. Cleavly had suggested, and because there was no other room vacant, they agreed. Frank's family consisted of fourteen year old Ethel, and twelve year old Rosie, who was delighted to have young John and baby Angela living with them. The sitting room was large and airy, with plenty of room for them all, while the wide open fireplace cheerfully burning a mixture of coal and applewood logs was warm and comforting.

The old house had not always been a farmhouse; built in the old Tudor style it was for many decades the residence of various squires of the village of Bradley Green. It was surrounded by many acres of land including a very large and unkempt garden, while a long stony drive led down to the road.

The heavy oak front door led into square black and white tiled hall, while a glass panelled door opposite the front door at the far end of the hall led into the gardens. The house was three storeys high, and Janie and John's bedroom was at the top of the house, while Rose and Frank with the girls slept on the first floor. On a tour of inspection Janie noticed that the very large windows of her brother's bedroom were protected by sturdy iron bars, and when she asked him, Frank said he thought the room was once a nursery.

To Janie's relief, young John soon recovered from his illness, so she took him to the village school, which was two miles away. Miss Jervis was the kindly teacher who had the task of teaching five to fourteen year old children, at which age they left school.

Janie missed her own home, but she realised that many people were homeless through the bombing, and that they were fortunate to have a roof over their heads. However, they did not altogether escape the war in the air, since even in the country they had to shelter from the stray bullets and spent cartridges which fell to earth from the 'dog-fights' overhead.

There was a rota of cleaning arranged between the various women tenants of the rooms, when the staircases and hall and landings had to be scrubbed, as they were all carpetless. Still, Janie got on well with the farm people, and eventually was allowed to use the large cooking range in the oldfashioned kitchen. Each mid-day she had a meal ready for the workers when they came up tired and hungry from the fields. Mrs. Cleavly was grateful for she was not much of a cook, while she noticed how clean and neat the kitchen looked these days.

Also, as Janie got known round the farms she took on the various mending and sewing jobs as all hands were busy on the land. She did not accept payment for this work, but there was always a packet of tea or a bit of sugar or butter and a few eggs to help out the meagre rations of the family. So, although life could be better, it could undoubtedly have been much worse, and she found that the days passed quickly enough as she did her work and looked after the children. She realised that she was coming to love the country with its clean fresh air, and when she went to the well across two fields to get the drinking water she loved to watch the birds in the nearby orchard and the cows and sheep peacefully living their lives in the fields. In this way she learnt to 'stand and stare' and somehow the Spirit World came very close to her.

One day it was her turn to clean the stairs, and as she scrubbed and sang softly to herself, she glanced up and saw 'Monsieur Lechum' standing in a bend in the stairs, looking at her with wide eyed surprise. His sudden appearance startled her and her heart jumped alarmingly. The two stared at each other, while she struggled to regain her composure. Then he gave her a half smile and slowly vanished from her sight. Janie realised he was still there although she could not see him, so, mustering up her courage, she told him she was pleased to see him and hoped he would come again; which indeed he did do, several times, and she grew quite used to seeing him around. Once or twice other people saw him, and commented on the strange man in fancy dress, but Janie said nothing about him, fearing people would not understand and would think her mad. John told her not to worry about it, as they had been told that M. Lechum would look after them during the war, and it did not matter what people thought – anyway, they wee always coming and going in that house, and so far, the farmer's family had shown no interest in the matter.

One day, Janie was in the wash-house doing the family washing. She stood at a concrete sink, rinsing clothes in a wooden tub, while behind her an old-fashioned boiler was coming up to the boil ready to receive the clothes to whiten them. She finished rubbing the dirt out of the garments, and threw them into the copper, pressing them down with the wooden copper stick.

Overhead, several planes were involved in the usual 'dog-fights'. Janie scarcely noticed them as she washed out the tub and pushed it to one side. As she did so, she heard a voice calling from the yard outside. "Mrs. Bailey, Mrs. Bailey, come here, quickly." Rather alarmed, she ran outside, looked around, but could see no-one. Puzzled, she turned to retrace her steps, when once more she heard the voice calling her, but this time it seemed further away, around the corner into the garden. She made her way there, following the path which led to the heavy oak front door which always stood open. The voice had ceased and all was silent except for the guns still firing overhead; she ran up the steps into the hall and called out, but there was no response, as everyone but herself was at work or working in the fields. Then suddenly she remembered little Angela who was asleep in her pram at the side of the wash-house. Alarmed, she ran quickly back, to find her little one still peacefully sleeping. She went into the wash-house, and gazed carefully around; the boiler was still bubbling away, the two empty buckets were still to one side of the sink where she had pushed them. Puzzled, she shrugged her shoulders, and bent down to pick up the buckets to fetch fresh water from the well. As she did so, her eyes fell on the surface of the sink. Two holes, newly made, were there, just where she had been standing. Janie felt the blood drain from her face, and her whole body trembled – but she was no longer so puzzled about the voice which had called her.

CHAPTER 21:

THE NURSERY BEDROOM.

When they had lived at the farm for about six months, Frank was fortunate enough to meet a farmer at the local inn who had a small cottage to let on the outskirts of the next village; he and his family duly moved out of the old house, so John asked Mr. Cleavly if he would allow him and his family to move down into the nursery bedroom. He gave his consent, and Frank helped John to bring down his beds and other furniture before he and his family left.

Janie was highly delighted with the arrangement, as there would now be more space for them all; also the wide picture window looked out onto the neglected garden, the very wildness of which added to its beauty. The room itself appealed to her. She thought of the children who might have played and slept there; where were they now, if they still lived? Maybe they were very old and if they came back to their once grand home they would be sad and shocked to see how it had degenerated to a shabby farmhouse. She shivered at the thought, and tried hard to imagine the laughter of the children as they played.

Some weeks went by, and Janie found herself more and more engrossed in the life of the surrounding countryside. She worked hard in whichever way she could to help in the farming community, and she made many friends. She, also, met one or two old people who knew the history of Bradley House and they told her many interesting stories, one of which was the tale of the five children who had all been stricken with a mysterious illness and had died one after the other. She was greatly saddened at this story, and came to regard her bedroom as a shrine to five little children.

Then one night something happened which made the young couple realise that the Spirit World was very near to them. They had gone to bed and the children were peacefully sleeping; Janie blew out the candle, which was on a table at the side of the bed and settled down to sleep. Suddenly, there was a loud bang at her side of the bed, children's laughing voices filled the rooms, and dancing feet ran into the centre of the carpet.

Both John and Janie sat upright in bed, alarmed and bewildered, and in the strong moonlight shining through the thin curtains saw five children, aged from about three to twelve years old, hands linked in a circle, as they danced to the old favourite, "Ring a ring of roses," their childish voices rising to a crescendo of song. Several nursery songs they sang as they danced, some of which Janie had never heard, then after about fifteen minutes, they ceased singing, formed into a line, the eldest being first, and came demurely up to the bed.

"Thank you, Madam.... Thank you, sir, for letting us play a little while in our old nursery, and, please may we come again?" John was lost for words, but his wife forced herself to speak, in a very small voice. "Yes, it was nice of you to come, I hope we will see you again," and before either of them could muster enough courage to speak again, the line of visitors dissolved into thin air. Janie pinched her arm to see if she were awake, then turned to her husband to note his reaction.

His eyes were large and staring, disbelief was in his face; then, he put out a hand and gently touched his wife, as if he could not believe that she was real; then at last he found his tongue.

"Good God! What was all that about …. how did all that happen? Their nursery? Why, this is our bedroom – and you told them to come again! Who are they, anyway?"

"This room was a nursery once and five children played here, but they died of a mysterious illness. I found that out from some of the old farmers round about. But why should they suddenly appear tonight? I don't know, we must ask them, when they come again."

"Come again? Why come again, why should they, what do they want?" spluttered John in his bewilderment.

Janie tried to remain calm as she searched her mind for an explanation. "I think," she said, "that those children are using the power that Leon Lechum uses to materialise, and it comes from either of us or both, and possibly even the children. If they do come again we must ask them."

John looked very thoughtful, "I wonder why Rose and Frank didn't say anything about this, they might know it would come as a shock to us."

"Oh! I don't suppose it happened to them, I don't think either of them are mediums. So one of us must be," replied Janie with a wisdom she did not feel.

"I wish to goodness I knew more about these things, we'll have to try to get hold of Jim to see if he can help us. In the meantime, if those children do come again, we'd better have a natter to the eldest one and see if he can enlighten us. And now we had better get some sleep or we won't be up in the morning."

But there was very little sleep for Janie that night as she lay turning the night's events over in her mind. She felt in her heart a vague excitement as she though of the five little figures dancing so happily in the centre of the room. What a pity they had been obliged to give up the circle, with such mediumship they could have produced wonderful phenomena. She longed to talk it over with Jim and other members of the circle. The next night the young couple retired to bed with a slight foreboding in their hearts. Janie was glad that their two children were sound asleep for she could not imagine what their reaction would be to having five other children playing in their bedroom in the middle of the night.

They had been in bed for about ten minutes, when the small explosion came at Janie's side of the bed and the excited voices of the visitors were heard. The same routine of the night before had occurred, but this time the moonlight was hidden behind clouds, so they could not see the children plainly.

John reached for the matches, determined to light the candle, but his wife stopped him. "Don't," she objected, "you may harm us, at least ask their permission." John hesitated, then whispered, "Alright, then you ask them."

Janie faltered, not knowing quite what to say. Then in a small voice she asked if they might light the candle as they could not see the children dancing as they had done the night before.

The eldest boy replied, "Oh, yes, Madam, just one candle, and thank you for wanting to see us."

The singing and dancing started, and little Angela stirred in her sleep. Soon she was wide awake, struggling to sit upright in her cot; her eyes sought the singing group and delight slowly spread over her little face. "Mommy, mommy, me play," she called out.

"No, no," her mother replied urgently, "If you get out of your cot the children will have to go; just lie quietly and watch them."

But Janie was all on edge; she had one eye on her daughter in case she tried to climb out of her cot, and one eye on the Spirit visitors in the centre of the carpet.

The fifteen minutes or so were soon up and the line of children came up to the bed. Janie was determined to question them. "What is your name?" she asked the eldest boy. "Richard, Madam," he replied. "Now, Richard, tell me, how are you able to show yourselves like this? Have you been here like this before we came?"

"We have been here many times, but not like this; until you came here, we were not seen or heard, now we have a teacher who has taught us how to use ectoplasm which comes from you, and your husband, and the children also help."

"But, why do you want to come back here, aren't you happy in your own world?"

"Oh, yes, we are very happy, and have a lovely home; but we were also very happy here in our earthly home and it seems that we left here so suddenly. You see, we see it as it was, not as it is now and it makes us happy, and I do hope that it makes you happy too, having us with you for a little while. Now we must go, the power is going. Goodbye," and as before the children melted away.

One day John came home from work and told his wife that he had been assigned to night work for a long stretch, seven nights in the week. Janie was apprehensive about being alone with the nightly visitors. Angela was awake most times, but some force seemed to keep her quiet as she lay and watched the children play; but not once had young John been disturbed and she wondered how she would cope with him if he did wake up, as they had never told him of the nightly visits. Her husband found a solution. He would tell young Richard, when next he came, to postpone his visits until the night work had finished. Janie felt rather mean about it, but she thought it was the best thing to do in the circumstances. In her later years, when she had got so used to Spiritual contacts, she deeply regretted turning away such wonderful phenomena; but at the time it happened she was new to the wonders of Spiritualism and she preferred companionship during its activities.

So the next time Richard appeared John explained their changed circumstances and hoped he would stop the visits until things were normal. Richard was silent for a moment and Janie was afraid he would disappear without speaking; she somehow felt his eyes searching her face and her heart sank.

"Alright, sir," he said, "we will do as you wish. Thank you for having us. When you are ready for us, we will come again, just send your thoughts to us." And the five children vanished. They were never seen again.

CHAPTER 22:

A HOUSE OF THEIR OWN.

Time went by and as far as the Midlands were concerned, the war quietened down and wearily, people tried to resume normal life again. The main setback was shortage of housing, so many homes had been destroyed or badly damaged in the blitz, and it seemed, even now, that it would be some time before building could start.

Janie longed for a little place of her own. The farm family were getting on each others nerves, and quarrelling was the order of the day. Her children were growing up and Janie did not like them to be in the atmosphere of aggression and swearing, so each day while the children were at school, she got out her old bicycle and toured the countryside looking for cottages to let. She and John had made up their minds never to go back to the town. They had both grown to love the country so much, but fate had other plans in store. Each day a prayer was sent up to the 'Powers that be' for help in finding their own home, but it seemed that the Almighty One was far too busy to pay attention to their pleas.

Then, one night, in the spring of 1944, Janie found herself in the Spirit World talking to her father. She was discussing with him her anxiety to get a cottage to rent; she had been everywhere, but she could not find one. "Do not despair," her father replied, "we are doing all we can to help. Remember hard what I am going to tell you. There is a smallholding coming up for sale, go and make enquiries, you will find your house in that direction. The name of the district is Hollberrow Green; Do not forget, Holberrow Green." Just then, Janie felt a pull from her body and knew she must get back, but as she awoke in bed, she could still hear her father's voice repeating the name of a place she had never heard of.

Over breakfast she told John who by now had grown quite used to his wife's Spiritual experiences. He said nothing for a moment or two, then he remarked that he had never heard the name either. "But this evening I'll go for a drink and ask some of the chaps." He came home in great excitement, not waiting for Frank who was playing a domino match with some of the older worthies. "You're right," he exclaimed, "I've found out where it is and there is a smallholding for sale, but nobody knows if the house is to be separated from the land. Tomorrow evening I'll borrow a bike off Bob Clevely and we'll go and see what's on."

Janie could hardly contain herself until her husband got home from work the next evening and had eaten his meal. After giving young John instructions about looking after little Angela until they returned home, the pair set off towards the general direction of Hollberrow Green. As they drew nearer to their goal they realised they had been there several times before. It was very isolated and the lane was little more than a cart-track, but they carried on until they came to a small farm house and a labourer's cottage, almost opposite.

Of course, they had no idea whether the locality was the district they had been looking for, because during the war all place names had been removed. But on going a few yards further on and turning a corner, they faced the front side of the house and the estate agent's notice that 'this desirable property for sale.' They dismounted from their cycles, and as they gazed around, Janie's heart sank. The notice read, "This desirable property for sale, together with so many acres of arable land." The residence was desirable all right, she would love it, but they could never hope to buy it, and she reckoned that even if they rented it they would find it far too expensive for them. Whatever was our Dad thinking about? He certainly had lost touch with earthly affairs. When next they met she would have to put him right.

John placed his cycle against the fence and marched up the long path to the front door, on which he knocked vigourously...... and he knocked and knocked and knocked, but no response came, so he turned and beckoned to his wife who timidly walked up the long path on tiptoe. "Why the hush-hush?" he asked impatiently, "there's no-one here, not a soul in sight. Let's have a peep through the window."

"Oh, no, it isn't right, perhaps someone is there and may have fallen asleep in a chair."

"Then if they are asleep, they won't see us, will they? I just want to see the size of the room." So saying, John cupped his hands on the window pane to shut out the reflection and gazed intently into the room.

"Good lord," he muttered, "they've already moved out, there are only a few odds and ends left lying about; but it's a lovely large square room, I wonder how many bedrooms there are? Quite four, I should think. Too large just for us, of course, but Barry and Maureen could come and live with us, and I know of another couple who would jump at the chance, and we could all share expenses."

Janie felt an icy hand clasp her heart, while she stared at her husband in amazement. "But I don't want to live with other people, I'm tired of sharing a house, I just want to live in a small cottage, two up and two down. Besides, you know I don't like Barry or Maureen, I certainly don't want to live with them. Anyway, if those folk have moved, they must have sold the house."

John was very angry; "I knew you'd be awkward," he spluttered, "When I told Barry at work today, that we were coming to see this place, he said they were looking for somewhere else to live, and if it was big enough they'd share it with us." Janie did not answer; a new sound broke on her ears, and she stared expectantly towards the lane. John heard it too, as he turned sharply round.

"Farm cart," he muttered, "must be coming here. Now perhaps, we'll get to know something."

The cart trundled slowly up to them, the elderly driver eyeing them curiously as he removed an old clay pipe from his mouth. "Bay 'ee looking for some'un?" he inquired, as he pulled up the horse. "Yes," replied John, "we were told that this smallholding was for sale, but, it looks as if we're too late."

"Aye, mabbe 'ee are. Why, did 'ee wan't t' buy it then?"

John looked a trifle uneasy. "Well, no; but we want somewhere to live, and we thought, perhaps the buyer may only need the land, and he may let the house to us."

"Aye, I see; but, I'm told a city woman 'as bought it for 'er son and 'is family to live 'ere, so I don't think as you'll be lucky."

"I see; thank you." John's voice was full of disappointment. "By the way, what is the name of this locality?"

"Why, don't 'ee know it? It be Hollberrow Green, a'course." And the old man chuckled as he ambled on his way.

"So much for your dreams; a waste of time it's all been. Next time you get information from the Spirit World, make sure you get all the details," and John rode on ahead of his crestfallen wife.

*   *   *

The following Saturday, John's sisters, Liz and Floss, were coming to spend the day with them, so Janie and the children walked the two miles to the bus terminus to meet them. Janie had been very miserable and disappointed over the outcome of her dream, while she and John had hardly spoken to each other, since that episode. She would certainly keep her dream wanderings to herself in future, but oh, how she would love another opportunity of a few minutes' talk with her father.

On the way home Liz and Janie walked on ahead of the others, and after the usual small talk, Liz said, "I suppose you would still like to find your own place?"

"Yes," replied Janie gloomily, "I've been everywhere, when I've had news of a cottage, but it's always been let to someone else."

"And I suppose you are still bent on staying in the country, or would you move back into the town?" inquired Liz, rather anxiously. Janie felt the tension in her voice and looked at her sharply.

"Don't tell me you know of somewhere in the town with all the house shortage?" Janie's voice was charged with disbelief. "Well, no, not exactly the town, but perhaps the Licky Hills. You see, Mrs. Jennings, who you know lives around the corner from us, has bought a smallholding for her son and family, and they live in the Licky Hills. She thinks there may be a chance of you getting their house." Janie stopped dead in her tracks. "And do you know where this smallholding is?"

Liz looked vague. "Somewhere Astwood Bank way, I think, or Redditch. But, Mrs. Jennings wants John to go to see her and she'll explain it all to him."

So that is how John came to be on his way to his old home locality, using up his precious petrol allowance, the next day. Mrs. Jennings greeted him warmly, and after making a cup of tea, settled down to talk. "You see," she explained, "My son Bill is heartily sick of factory work, and after the war would like to work on the land. He's always had a yen for the country; it's in his blood I suppose, our ancestors were farmers. So, Bill being the only one, I thought I would spend some of my savings and buy him a smallholding ready for the end of the war, which I don't think will be long in coming now."

She paused for breath and John jumped in. "Mrs. Jennings, where's this smallholding? I'm not being nosy, but it's important to Janie and me. You see, she had a dream and I'm wondering...." His voice trailed off, he suddenly felt a fool, especially as his old neighbour looked at him with a half smile on her face.

"Right John, now suppose you tell me, and we'll see if that dream has given your wife true information."

John shifted uneasily in his chair. He was wishing he had kept the dream to himself; then he thought, well, here goes, can't do much harm, her knowing. "Hollberrow Green," he blurted out, "but we've never heard of the place before now."

Mrs. Jennings burst out laughing, for now she felt reassured she had picked the right one for the plan she had in mind.

"Absolutely correct," she replied, "now listen to what I have to say. Bill rents his house, on the Licky Hills. Beacon Hill is the name of the road – from a woman named Mrs. Cornforth, who lives on the Rednal side of the hills. Now Bill wants to move out in three weeks time, so you and your family could move in during that time and stay put when Bill and his family have gone."

John looked doubtful. If they gave up living at Bradley House, then got thrown out from Beacon Hill, where on earth would they go? He voiced his thoughts to his companion and her reply was full of confidence. "Don't forget the squatters right, which came out with all the bombing of the houses. If you lose your home through air-raids you have a right to take over any empty house available, or part of a house, and you lost yours through bombing, didn't you?"

"Yes," replied John, slowly, "All the doors and windows were blown out, in the middle of winter, too, it was impossible to live there. That's why we've had to stay in the one room in the country. But now the children are older and need their separate rooms, so it would be a blessing if we could get this house. Yes, it's certainly worth the risk. Do you think next weekend will be alright to move in?"

"Yes," replied Mrs. Jennings, "I'll let Bill know. And don't forget, once you are in stay put. You may have a bit of a skirmish, but you my as well be the next tenant as anyone else."

John thanked his friend and made his way home as quickly as possible. His wife was impatiently waiting for him to return. Her face clouded over somewhat as John unfolded his news. She hated taking chances, but she realised that if the house were left empty, there would be a crowd of homeless people waiting to take it over. Also, thinking of her father's insistence in her dream, she felt that the Spirit World would be behind them in helping them out.

So, for the next few days Janie spent the time sorting out their few belongings and packing what she could, while John made arrangements to find enough petrol for the journey and a farm worker he knew who could lend them a farm lorry for the furniture. Saturday afternoon saw them on the road towards heavens knows what, and suddenly Janie felt sick with apprehension. She pinned her mind on her father's voice and his insistence that she follow up the lead he had given her, namely, Hollberrow Green. Neither she or John or any of their friends had ever heard of the name before. So she thought her dream must be prophetic and to this extent she had demonstrated that her ability to contact the Spirit World must be real. So she told herself she must have more faith in the loved ones who were trying to help them.

At last they arrived at "Melita", the name of the house, which was situated half way up the Beacon Hill, on the Rubery side of the Lickey Hills. Melita was one of ten houses, all well built with various styles of front windows and long front gardens leading to the main door. On the opposite side of the lane were half a dozen Edwardian houses standing in their own grounds. Janie loved the country aspect and the grand view of the hills, only about ten minutes walk away.

Bill Jennings quickly helped them to get their belongings inside the house, then promptly locked all doors and windows. Then he helped his two friends put up the beds and arrange the furniture, his own belongings having been removed the day before.

"Now," he said, "the folk next door are friends of Mrs. Cornforth, the landlady, and they are sure to have phoned to let her know that I have moved out; and now they'll let her know that you have moved in. Whoever comes here, tell them you will only admit the owner of the house and you would like to talk to her. She's all right really, rather religious, but I think she'll listen to you; I should let Janie talk to her, I think she'll influence her." After this, Bill took his leave and went on his way.

Janie set about getting her family a hot meal, and she found it strange cooking on a gas stove after using an oil cooker for so long. She gazed around the kitchen and felt a warm thrill of excitement at the thought of being in a house once again; she would have loved to have opened the back door to see what the garden was like, but she knew she daren't.

The meal was eaten and she was washing up, when she heard a loud knock on the front door. She quickly dried her hands, and ran in to John who was in the living room. He put a finger to his lips and went quietly out into the hall. The knock was repeated on the door, but much louder this time, Janie's heart was pounding so quickly in her throat, she thought she would choke. John went up to the door and lifted the flap of the letterbox.

"Who is there?" he called out.

"I am Edward Cornforth," a voice said back, "the son of the owner of the house, I want to know who you are and what you are doing there?"

"I am John Bailey and I am here with my wife and two young children. We have nowhere to live, I would very much like to talk to your mother, will you please bring her along?"

"I represent my mother, so you open the door and talk to me."

"No, I can't do that," John called out, "I shall only open the door to Mrs. Cornforth." So saying John replaced the flap and walked away from the door. He and Janie ran to the front window, to see a middle-aged, well-dressed man walk slowly down the garden path to a waiting car at the gate.

Next morning, Janie had cleared away after breakfast, and made the beds and was getting the children settled with their toys, when a car drove into the drive and the same man who had been there the evening before, got out to help an elderly lady to alight. John was in the front room and looking through the window guessed the owner of the house had called. He went out into the hall and was joined by his wife. They waited for the knock on the door, before John with a breathless "Here goes," opened it, while Janie stood back, her face ashen.

John stared at the visitors, the ability to speak having left him, while they stared back, their expressions a mixture of curiosity and aggressiveness. Then the lady spoke very quietly, "I am Mrs. Cornford, this is my son Edward; may we come in?"

John stood back, holding the door wide. "Yes, of course," he stuttered, "Please come in." He shoved them into the front room and motioned Janie to follow. "This is my wife," he explained, "will you please sit down?" The pair hesitated, then, looking round, Mrs. Cornford sat down and her son followed suit.

"Now tell me," she asked, "Who are you, why are you here, and where is Mr. Jennings?" John took a deep breath and began to talk. He told them the whole story from the time they were bombed out, how they had lived since, and now that the children were growing older they needed extra room. He said that Mr. Jennings had kindly offered them accommodation so that they could be near the town to find a house. In the meantime, Mr. Jennings had gone to help his mother who had bought a smallholding in the country.

There was silence for a few moments while the visitors took in what they had been told. Mrs. Cornford turned to Janie; "Will you allow me to see the rest of the rooms in the house? I've a reason for asking."

Janie glanced across at her husband and received his nod of consent. She took her visitor into the dining room and then into the little morning room and the kitchen beyond. How glad she was that she had had time to clean up and to make the beds to leave everything tidy; it was sure to give a good impression.

Upstairs, Mrs. Cornford paid particular attention to the bedrooms, then she crossed over to the window overlooking the garden; there, she stood so long in silent contemplation that Janie grew uneasy and apprehensive. When at last she turned away from the window, she gazed long and earnestly at her young companion's face. Janie felt her colour rise as she forced herself to stare back; she sent out a silent prayer, "Please God, do let her understand."

At last Mrs. Cornforth spoke. "I notice you only have beds made up for you and your husband and the two children," she queried, "Be frank with me.... what are Mr. Jennings' plans?"

For a moment Janie hesitated, then suddenly she knew what she must do. She told the older woman what Mr. Jennings and her husband had planned.

"So, you are telling me that Jennings has given up the tenancy of this house and does not intend coming back here to live. I sincerely hope you mean that. He has not been a good tenant. He has kept fowl and chickens in the empty bedrooms and the garden is a disgrace. I have taken a liking to you. There's a good spiritual glow around you. Promise me you will take care of the house and keep it nice, and I will gladly accept you as my tenant. Come along, let's go and have a word with your husband, I must have it in writing that Jennings has given up the tenancy of this house. I do not want him back here again."

Janie could not believe her ears; she simply floated down the stairs. John stared into her eyes and knew something had transpired. Mrs. Cornford sat down and looked across at John.

"Young man, your wife has told me everything. I understand your difficulties and I am willing to help. Promise me that you will do something to tidy up that garden .... you have your young son to give you a hand ..... and I will accept you as my tenant. Get in touch with Jennings and tell him to send me his written notice to quit. You can pay me my rent on the first Monday in every month. Your wife can bring it. I will give you my address, I live the other side of Beacon Hill."

She stood up and prepared to take her leave; John followed her as in a dream. As he opened the door for his new benefactor, she turned to him and held out her hand. "Glad to have met you, Mr. Bailey. Oh, by the way, I am raising your rent by five shillings." Then with a half smile she added, "I hope we have a long and friendly partnership."

After the front door had closed, the young couple stared speechless at one another, afraid to move in case the 'dream spell' would be broken. Then Janie thought of her father and his "Holberrow Green" and she sent out a thought.... "from the bottom of my heart, thanks, Dad."

CHAPTER 23:

NEW AND BROKEN CIRCLES.

Janie was thrilled with the house and all the convenience it provided. There was a large cooking range in the morning room, and a gas stove in the kitchen, a good pantry and cupboard space.

Of course, the range needed coal and wood, which was rationed and hard to get, but young John found he could collect lots of twigs and small rotting branches lying about on the ground when he took Bruce, their Welsh collie dog, on a run over the hills. But there was no more toiling across two fields and an orchard to the fresh water well, to haul back two buckets of water. True, the rain water well had been in the back yard of the farm and near to the kitchen. But three and a half years of lowering the heavy bucket and swinging it full of water by its thick coil rope to the top of the well, had left Janie with a permanently aching back.

The furniture was only sufficient to furnish one room downstairs. But the empty room was useful for the children to play in when it was raining and upstairs they all had a comfortable room to sleep in. She thought often of the large bedroom in the farmhouse and of the five spirit children who used to visit them; also of Leon the French cavalier whom she had not seen for some time. This fact set her thinking that perhaps the war would soon be at an end, so Leon did not have to worry about her safety any longer. She fervently hoped that she would meet all of them again some day, perhaps, when she would have more opportunity of meeting spirit folk and becoming used to them.

Now and again, Jim and Rita Arnold and other members of the circle came to visit them and they would discuss the circle and when they would be able to sit again. Although Janie and John had moved nearer to Birmingham, Rita and Jim had moved away to the east of the city and obtaining petrol for the little motor cycle on which they would have to travel was the problem. John was allowed a small ration to get him to work, but there was little left over for other journeys. Janie, over optimistic, vowed that if Spirit wished them to start sitting again, they would remove the problems.

Spirit or not, in a short while, John was offered a seat in the car of a neighbour who worked at the same factory, so John's petrol was used for the circle journey.

Janie was thrilled and excited at the thought of sitting in a circle again; she was hoping that they wuld be able to start where they had left off with their old circle way back in the early 1940's, but Jim seemed dubious about this as they would not be sitting with the same friends. For a time it would just be Jim and

Rita, John and Janie. So until Frank and Rose could move back to Birmingham again, and the other members, who were held up with work and family commitments were free to sit again, the Circle would not be the same as it had been. However, Jim thought that they would be holding the fort, so to speak, and they could be developing spiritually towards the time their friends could join them.

So, time went on, until there seemed to be a change in the air which affected everybody. War work palled a little, while people stood in groups and talked excitedly. People were expecting the war to end and joyous expectancy was in every face.

But the circle carried on and although nothing spectacular had occurred, the quiet happiness and the feeling of being with something good and loving, filled the four sitters with joy and anticipation.

And then it came; the war was over, and people could begin to live a peaceful life once more. But of course it was not as easy as all that. The lives of most people had changed quite drastically. Many had lost their homes, and their families were tragically diminished through enemy action. Moreover many people were out of work, until the factories could retool from war production to peacetime working. Houses would have to be rebuilt, and children brought back from the evacuation areas.

John was out of work for a time. Then he realised that many houses needed electrical repairs, so, on a friend's advice, he went into the city of Birmingham to find out the wholesalers who were still in business selling electrical materials. After much talk with those "in the know", he set up in his own business, and thereafter, worked very hard and all hours. Janie helped out whenever she could, attending to the office work, keeping the books and looking after the customers' requirements. She loved the shop work, but the office work she found dull and monotonous, and invariably went home with a headache.

Then one day they heard from Frank that he and Rose and their two girls were moving back to Birmingham, and that when they were settled, he and Rose hoped to join the circle once again. Janie was overjoyed, and the next time she and John saw Jim and Rita, found they were both looking forward to the extra sitters. Eventually, Rose's sister and her husband joined, making eight in all, which was a good number for a physical circle. Every week, at the end of the sitting, "Great White Cloud". Jim's Guide would speak to them, telling them how they had progressed, and sometimes giving them advice if they were in doubt about anything. After a time Janie began feeling fingers were touching her head and gently stroking her face. At first she was startled, but when the guide came through at the end of the sitting, he explained that they were her loved ones who wished her to know they were present and were helping her to develop her Spiritual work. After this, her nervousness left her, and she looked forward to the contact with her loved one, whom she now knew to be her mother.

Life went on in this manner for several months, then one evening after the circle, Jim told his friends that he and his wife were moving back to Kings Heath and that the circle would have to close for a short while. Of course, there was dismay and disappointment amongst them, but Jim promised them that as soon as possible he would resume the circle.

They had to be content with this; they all realised that trying to keep a circle going with the same sitters was very difficult. Family commitments would interrupt attendence and sitters would disappear from the scene and new friends sought who could take their place. In future years they all found out that Spirit Workers used this method to change the sitters when any did not blend or harmonise with the rest of the sitters; it was all a case of vibrations from each sitter blending with each other. Without harmony, they and the Spirit Workers would be wasting their time. this was one reason why development of physical phenomena took so many years to accomplish. The interruptions did not come from the Spirit Workers, but they could only work with a circle of sitters of the correct vibrations: It was very difficult to find from five to eight people whose vibrations blended in the way they should to create the harmony needed; for harmony was the key necessary to unlock the door between the two worlds and to establish communication. Also, there must not be discord or bad feeling of any kind amongst the sitters; harmony simply meant enjoying each others company and for an hour feeling happy and carefree. Spirit did the work, the sitters supplied the right conditions. One other thing – lively music should be played and the sitters could sing if they wished.

Eventually, Jim and Rita were settled in their new home and the circle once again restarted. Then one evening, some months later, a whisper was heard, and someone said that the voices had started. But Janie felt a wave of disappointment flow over her. She could not account for it, as she understood that the Spirit voices could only whisper in the initial stage.

When Jim came out of trance, he was very excited at the new development, and over the cups of tea and sandwiches, could not stop talking about it. Janie sat quietly, trying to puzzle out her attitude of mind; she glanced across at her brother and wondered what he thought of the whisper, but he seemed to her to be avoiding her gaze. On the way home she questioned John, but after a short silence he shrugged his shoulders and said that time would tell ..... the voice would either get stronger or fade altogether. She thought her husband was right and she was determined to push the strange feeling from her mind and look forward to the next sitting as usual.

In time the whisper did grow stronger and words could be identified, but the words were trivial and uninformative and when questioned as to who the communicator was, the voice faded away altogether. Jim refused to be daunted, saying that there was sure to be 'teething troubles'. Janie said she was surprised that Spirit would have 'teething troubles', she imagined that they could over-come things like that. Jim gave her a long look and stated that they were not dealing with magicians, that they were only one step ahead of themselves, and that even the Spirit people had to contend with difficulties and setbacks when working with the Earth folk.

At the next circle, the voice was absent, but most of the sitters received touches on their hands; as the evening wore on Janie felt something gently caress the top of her hand, but instead of soft warm fingers, there was a rough-ness like a hand in a knitted wool glove. Also, there was no happy affection coming with the touch, like there had been at Leslie Flint's sittings. Again, that sensation of disappointment came over her, and her heart sank. What was wrong? Why did she feel like this? And why had this once-lovely circle sud-denly lost its appeal, with its warmth and love flowing from the world of Spirit.

Over the refreshments, after the circle, the touches were discussed, and var-ious descriptions were given and Janie noticed that several had felt the rough-ness. Jim was asked for an explanation and he said he thought the ectoplasm was not refined, and it was rough instead of smooth as it should be.

Several sittings were held, but to Janie's mind something was not quite right, then one evening Frank and Rose came to have a chat with John and Janie, and what Frank said startled his sister greatly. She could not speak; her head was in a whirl, and she could not collect her thoughts, in the midst of her confusion, she heard John say, "Yes, Frank, I suspected something was going on and I know Janie feels that something is wrong."

All three of them looked at Janie who sat silent and palefaced. Forcing her-self to speak, she turned to her brother: "Oh, no, Frank. Such a thought never entered my head. I do not think that Jim is faking; I feel that something is wrong, but not that."

Frank seemed certain in his accusations, and firmly stated that he was going to see Jim and tell him of their doubts and ask him to give up sitting in the cabinet, to let one of the other sitters take his place.

The outcome of it all, was that Jim appeared very hurt and indignant and refused to sit with Frank at all, but he said he would welcome Janie and John as usual. Within the next few days, a letter arrived from Jim inviting John and Janie to go on sitting with him and Rita to form a new circle, but on no account did he want Frank and Rose and their relatives sitting with them. Instead of replying to the letter, John decided to call to see Jim. After all, they were friends and had enjoyed happy hospitality at their home. Janie went with him, but she felt very miserable and apprehensive on the journey. Oh, why did these these things happen? Why did Jim have to pretend? If indeed he did. She remembered her own felings and the absence of love coming from the touches, and last of all, the rough woolly caress which made her shrink and which Frank and the others said was a physical hand in a thick woollen glove.

They had all been prepared to sit and wait for the true phenomena. It was no hardship, as the evening always turned out friendly and enjoyable. Now, if pretence had been employed, the Spirit World would not co-operate with such sitters; they would be wasting their time trying to develop such a circle.

Jim and Rita received them cordially and Janie relaxed a little. After the usual trivial conversation, Jim broached on Frank's accusation, asking them what they thought about it. John looked at his wife, hesitated, then clearing his throat, looked straight at their inquirer. "Honestly speaking, Jim, we don't quite know what to make of it. Remember, Frank isn't the only one thinking as he does, Janie and I have been puzzled for some weeks at the change in the phenomena. Although we didn't like it, we didn't know if it was part of the usual development. So we didn't say anything. But not for one moment did we suspect that you...you," he hesitated, unsure how to proceed.

Jim interrupted, impatiently, "I know, I know, that I was faking it. And do you also, think that I was pretending," he turned abruptly to Janie, who was almost startled out of her wits.

"No, no," she stammered, "It was all so different and I didn't like it, especially the rough hand; before, the touches had been so soft and gentle; but I never dreamt it was you, and I can't believe it now."

"Neither can I," John murmured.

Jim turned to them, speculatively. "Rough hand, what do you mean by that?"

"Well, we assumed it was a hand, with thick fingers and rough in texture, I can't think how else to describe it ...." John's voice trailed off in uncertainty.

"Oh, perhaps Frank thought I was masquerading in woollen gloves, or such like." Jim's voice trailed off bitterly.

John looked sharply at him, his eyes seeking to penetrate his mind. Janie, glancing at him, saw him change. He stood resolutely to his feet and buttoned his coat. "Come along, Janie," he said, "there's no need to prolong this talk." He turned to Jim. "We do not wish to sit without Frank and Rose; we leave it to you to think it over. If we do sit again, I for one would like a change of medium. We'll be in touch. Thank you, for seeing us. Goodnight."

On the way home the pair sat in silence. Janie knew something had upset her husband, for there was a look on his face that she did not like; but something forbade her to question him.

As soon as they entered the house, John went to the telephone and dialled a number. As soon as it was answered, he said: "Oh, hello Rose, John speaking. Is Frank at home? I'd like a word with him." After a pause, John resumed. "Hello, Frank, we have been to see Jim, and what I want to know is.... did you mention a woollen glove to him? No? Well, he suggested it to me, and to my mind it sounds suspicious. I told him we would not sit without you four, and if we did sit we would want another sitter in the cabinet."

John listened a while longer, then put down the phone. He turned to his wife, "Don't worry anymore about all this. We are certainly not going to waste our time sitting with someone who may not be doing the right thing. Frank says they will make arrangements to form another circle at his house. He will let us know how things go."

Accordingly, after two or three weeks, Frank let them know the room was ready, and the new circle started its development with Frank in the cabinet. After about four months, Frank showed signs of going into trance, which delighted the rest of the sitters, as it meant that soon they would have a guide controlling his medium and talking to them, giving them instructions on sitting correctly and other matters.

In due course, the guide was able to speak through his medium, and he told his listeners that when on earth, he was a North American Indian of the Cherokee Tribe.

Janie began to see clairvoyant pictures of "Soaring Eagle" as he stood a little to one side of his medium. His figure was tall and slim, his features firm yet gentle, the eyes dark and penetrating, filled with love and friendship. The sitters regarded him as a very dear friend and loved to hear his discourses at the end of the sitting when he controlled his medium.

Then, one circle night, some months later, Janie was aware of a beautiful silver light build up in the darkness, quite close to her. Spellbound, she watched as the light formed itself into a bridge over which a figure walked. As it drew nearer to Janie, she realised it was the form of a Chinaman, dressed in splendid apparel, the kimono a wonderful purple colour. He stood in front of Janie for a moment, then faded away. She told the others what she had seen, but no-one could offer an explanation. At the next sitting, Janie saw him again, but this time, the kimono was of a different colour, a beautiful lavender shade.

And so it went on for twelve weeks, but each week the colours were different. Janie asked "Soaring Eagle" for an explanation, and he said that the Chinaman was a guide of one of the sitters and the colour of his raiment was the colours of his aura, which meant he was a highly developed soul.

CHAPTER 24:

THE SANCTUARY AT 'PINEWOODS'.

About this time, one of the sitters, a Mrs. Fisher, had a teenage niece living with her who had not been well, and the doctor suggested that she should go to the seaside, preferably Blackpool, for a few days. Although it was the beginning of April, and still rather cold, Mrs. Fisher decided it was a good idea. So, packing a bag for a few days, off she went with her niece in tow. After booking in at a hotel for the period necessary, the two set out for the local Spiritualist church, to see what the programme was for the weekend. To Mrs. Fisher's delight, she found that Helen Duncan, the then famous Physical Phenomena medium, would be working. She was able to get a ticket for the evening session, which, because of the events which followed in the near future, convinced Mrs. Fisher that the Spirit World took a hand in all the arrangements for visiting the seaside town. To be able to obtain a ticket at such short notice, for such a famous medium, was unheard of.

After a successful sitting, Mrs. Fisher sat back and sighed with evident satisfaction, when she noticed the lady next to her was regarding her smilingly. She nodded in response, and the two started to talk. "Wonderful, wasn't it?" offered Mrs. Fisher, "Is this your first time?" "With this medium, yes, but not with the phenomena. I come from Nottingham, and I have a friend who is a marvellous medium and I have witnessed many times the most extraordinary phenomena."

Mrs. Fisher sat up and took notice; opportunity was a fine thing, and she did not wish to lose anything. So, she put her questions. What was the medium's name, where did she live, and was it possible to obtain a sitting? The medium's name was Mrs. Isa Northage, and she lived at Bulwell, Nottingham. Yes, it was possible to get a sitting, but there was always a long waiting list. Mrs. Northage's chief Spirit Helper was a doctor who, when on earth, had been a surgeon at one of the London hospitals and he always took charge of the requests for sittings. He made it his business to find out the type of person or persons making the requests, and their reasons for them. He highly prized his medium, and he protected her accordingly as the wrong sitter could play havoc with her health.

The lady wrote down the name and address involved and Mrs. Fisher left the meeting walking on air. As soon as she got home after the short holiday, she sent her request to Mrs. Northage, stating the names of the circle members and that they desired help for their newly formed circle and saying that they hoped they would once again meet their loved ones who had passed to the world of Spirit. To their amazement and joy, they quickly received a reply booking their sitting for the month ahead, and the letter was signed, "Doctor Reynolds." .

They were all greatly excited and thought the date of the sitting would never arrive, which was the middle of May, 1948. At last the great day arrived and they all set out in two motor cars. On arrival they were shewn into a nicely furnished sitting room and after a few moments a tallish lady entered the room to welcome them. Somehow, Janie was thrilled at the sight of her; her face was gentle but also strong and shrewd. She told them that she must prepare for the sitting, while they drank the tea she would send in.

After about half an hour, another lady entered the room; she told the friends that she was Mrs. Difford, Mrs. Northage's daughter. She asked them to follow her, and she led them through the house to the garden at the back. Taking a path at the side of the lawn they came to a cedar-built shed, which acted as a sanctuary and seance room. At one end was an altar, on which rested a large wooden cross and at each side of it, two lovely vases filled with beautiful red roses. A thin dark curtain was hung across one corner, which made do as a cabinet for the medium to sit protected from the light, which could prove harmful.

In the centre of the room was a circle of ten chairs, and Mrs. Difford explained that a Mr. Stocks would be sitting with them. In a few moments he entered the room and welcomed them cordially, bidding them to be seated, while he and Mrs. Difford sat one either side of the cabinet.

The red light was extinguished, then Mr. Stocks opened in prayer, after which a hymn, "Nearer my God to thee," was sung. As they reached the last line, one of the three trumpets, which stood on the floor in the centre of the circle, rose up into the air, and a young girl's voice greeted them. She said she knew they had come on a long journey to be with them, and she hoped that they all would enjoy the sitting. She told them that her name was Ellen Dawes, and that she acted as receptionist for Dr. Reynolds. She had to ensure that all was well with the sitters and that the suitable power had built up for the seance to commence.

Then, a second trumpet floated upwards and a man's voice greeted them. He introduced himself as Dr. Reynolds and spoke to each sitter in turn. Mrs. Fisher told him that she was the person who had written and she thanked him for so soon giving them a sitting and all her friends murmured their thanks.

For three very short hours, loved ones came and went, but what made it so interesting was the fact that as all of the sitters were related, most of the spirit communicators were known to them. Janie was overjoyed when she heard her mother's voice calling to her loud and clear. The voice did not come through the trumpet, but at her side. Then suddenly she saw her mother with arms outstretched. Janie gave a cry of joy while she rose to her feet and embraced the lovely figure; clasped in each others' arms, mother and daughter kissed, while tears trickled down each face and intermingled.

Oh yes, spirits do weep on occasion, for in these respects they are just the same as when on earth. Meeting a loved one for the first time after a long separation, the joy and happiness is overwhelming and the tears cannot be checked. After she had composed herself a little, Janie asked her mother all the usual questions – was she happy, did she live in a lovely house with a beautiful garden and what did she do to occupy her time?" Her mother laughed and explained that she was quite happy and loved her new life, which was so different from earth life, with its trials and pain and suffering. She said she worked helping little children who had passed over tragically, to adapt to their new life and to forget the horror of their passing. Also, she, with others took the little ones back to their earth homes, to reunite them with their loved ones for a short time. Sometimes, the little ones are upset to find their parents grieving and unable to feel the little arms around their neck, or the childish voice speaking.

At another subsequent sitting Janie's mother brought two five year olds who had recently passed over through drowning, and who wanted to let their parents understand that they still lived on and were being looked after by people who loved them. They had been taken to their homes and could not understand why their parents could not see them or feel their arms around them; the mothers in particular were grieving badly, and were building up a barrier that prevented them from being aware of their children's presence. Janie's mother gave her the addresses in question, and after putting together two suitable letters Janie wrote her own address on the back of the envelopes for return if not delivered. The outcome was that one reply was received, thanking her for her kind letter, and the mother said she would try to control her sorrow and remain calm that she might become aware of her little son's presence. The whole letter felt so cold and detached that Janie had the feeling that she was being kindly brushed aside as an insane person. There was no reply to the other letter, neither was it returned.

Towards the end of his first sitting with Mrs. Northage, Dr. Reynolds spoke to tell them that the power was diminishing and the hour was late and they had a long journey in front of them. They all thanked Dr. Reynolds for the wonderful time they had experienced, and Janie added tht she hoped they would meet him and Mrs. Northage sometime again in the future. Janie felt a hand on her arm and a warm and friendly pressure given; the Doctor's voice rang out, "Mrs. Bailey, you and I will meet many times in the future and you will help me to do my healing work when the time is ready. I am so glad that we have at last met."

CHAPTER 25:

EARTHLY AND SPIRITUAL SURGERY.

Towards the autumn of that year, Janie began to feel very run down and "achey"; then about November, she developed intense pain down the back of her right thigh. She went to see her doctor, who diagnosed sciatica and gave her treatment accordingly. Over the next three months several remedies were tried but Janie found little relief. Then about January 1949, she went again to her doctor and he gave her a new prescription to try, and he asked her if she found no relief, would she go to a consultant the next week. Janie agreed; but that same evening, when she was getting ready for bed, she lifted her arm while brushing her hair, and felt a sharp pain under her arm. She cried out, and John asked her what was wrong. She told him, and he came over to her. He felt gently under the arm and down the side of the breast. What he found gave him great cause for alarm. There was deep anxiety in his face. "You must go to the doctor in the morning and ask him to examine you," he told his wife quietly. "But John, I can't do that, I only went this morning and doctor gave me some new ointment to try; he said if I'm no better next week he wants me to go to see a consultant at the Orthopaedic Hospital in Broad Street."

"Janie, you've got a nasty lump under your arm, but the main part of it is in the breast; it may not be anything to be alarmed about, but we must not neglect it." Janie looked at her husband and his stern expression made her heart sink. He was not an alarmist, and she knew he was right.

The next morning was Saturday, but Janie knew the surgery was open. She explained to the Doctor the reason for her visit, and he looked searchingly at her. After the examination, he said he must make a phone call; his call was put through and he asked for "Mr. Samuel Davidson's secretary." When he had made some arrangements, he put down the phone and turned to his patient. "I have booked an appointment for you to see a Mr. Samuel Davidson at the General Hospital, at ten o'clock on Monday morning. Don't worry about it, he's a very nice man, he will help you a lot."

So Janie kept her appointment and had her examination. She found Mr. Davidson a very kind and understanding man; he told her that she needed a major operation 'as all was not well inside'. Then he told her that he would like her to return to the hospital on the next Wednesday morning, to see a Mr. Baines about the lump in the breast. He said they would send for her when a bed was ready.

Mr. Baines received her kindly, and after his examination, which included measurements, explained to her that she had a large lump in each breast, one measuring three and one half inches, while the other was slightly smaller. Janie sat silent and stunned, she didn't know what to say; she could not bring herself to ask the dreadful question, but she felt she knew the answer.

He told her that he knew that Mr. Davidson would carry out an operation, then afterwards, she would be removed to his ward, that he might operate to remove the lumps. He hastened to add, that of course, she would remain with Mr. Davidson until she had regained sufficient strength for the second operation.

The next week found Janie at the Orthopaedic Hospital in Broad Street to see a Mr. T. S. Donovan. He put his patient through various exercises to try to locate the pain in the thigh. At last she was taken to be X-rayed and when the film came through Mr. Donovan called to two colleagues to whom he showed the X-ray. He lifted it high in the air facing a window at the back of the cubicle where Janie was waiting; the film showed above the height of the curtain surrounding the cubicle, giving Janie an excellent view of it. She did not understand it, but she noticed a dark shadow about as large as the palm of her hand, in the groin of her body. "Oh," she exclaimed, "What is that shadow, there on my groin?" The three doctors turned sharply and stared at the peeping young woman. Then Mr. Donovan called to the nurse in charge to bring his patient to his table, and he questioned her about her interview with Mr. Davidson at the General Hospital. Janie explained that he had told her that he must operate and he would send for her when a bed was ready. Mr. Donovan exploded a little, and he looked crossly at the nurse and shook his head. "My dear," he turned to his patient, "You are very seriously ill; you should be in hospital now, and surgery will put you right again, but there should not be any delay, I will get in touch with Mr. Davidson myself."

Janie left the hospital, her head in a whirl; she could not believe that she was the patient, she felt that another person was involved and she was a mere onlooker. She hardly noticed the journey home. Her thoughts were on the future, the family and especially Angela who by now was a growing girl of eleven years old; she was at an age when she needed a mother's care and attention.

Suppose things went wrong, what would happen to the child? Young John was just turned eighteen and was away somewhere in Norfolk doing his two years National Service in the R.A.F.

She did not rightly know how her husband felt about her news; but he got up from his chair and left the room, his face white and set.

The days and weeks went by, but she had no news from the hospital. She only realised that she was feeling very low and ill; she had no interest in food and had to force herself to eat for the sake of Angela. Once, when she was feeling extra weak and poorly, she turned and saw the child looking at her, the tears slowly falling from her cheeks.

A few days later, she was slowly making her way down the hill to the village to do some shopping, for she was determined to carry on as usual, when a car passed her going up the hill, and the driver glanced at her sharply and nodded his head. She recognised Professor Webster, the pathologist, who was a neighbour and friend. Janie glanced back and saw him turn into her own driveway; she guessed he wanted to see John about some electrical work and knew he would catch him during the lunch period. She thought no more of it, but when she got back home she found her husband still there waiting for her. He told her that Professor Webster was furious at the delay in the hospital sending for her, and he had gone straight away to the General Hospital. The result was that later that afternoon, a telegram arrived telling Janie that a bed was ready and would she be at the hospital the next morning at ten o'clock.

The next month proved a great ordeal for Janie, but she met with every kindness and consideration from the hospital staff. Surgery was carried out two days after entering hospital.

Sometime later, she found out that there had been great upset in the theatre, her breathing had stopped for quite four minutes, and desperate efforts were carried out to re-start it again. Janie only remembered that she had been with her mother, who constantly urged her to remain near her body as Doctor Reynolds was working with Mr. Davidson in the effort to restart her heart. Janie remembered pleading with her mother to take her away to let her rest as she was experiencing great fatigue; her mother clasped her gently in her arms, giving her great comfort and she knew no more.

The operation was performed on May 13, 1949 at nine o'clock. Mr. Davidson remained with his patient all night until he considered her out of danger the next day. Janie woke up once, very briefly, and was aware of a young nun dressed in white, sitting next to the bed. She vaguely thought she must be one of the helpers from a local convent who came in at times to sit with the very ill patients. But the tiredness and utter weakness she felt prevented her from asking questions, or indeed speaking at all and she floated away into utter oblivion. She remained like that for several days, waking up a brief intervals, and being aware of her watching nun; but always she succumbed to sleep with a sense of relief and confidence in her watching companion.

The next time she opened her eyes, the sister of the ward was at her bedside and she noticed that the nun was no longer there. Sister spoke to her quietly as she arranged the pillows to make her patient comfortable. Janie did indeed feel better, the utter wearines having left her. She glanced at the now empty chair, and enquired if the nun would return again. The sister looked surprised and shook her head, "No, my dear," she replied, "there are no nuns in the hospital, you must be dreaming." Janie was puzzled, the nun had seemed very real, and she had seen her several times. Somehow, she thought, perhaps she was working with Dr. Reynolds.

When she had been in the hospital nearly one month, Mr. Baines, the consultant she had seen about the growths in the breast, came to see her and expressed his pleasure to see she was making progress, however slowly. Then he told her that his former plan to carry out surgery on her, as soon as she had somewhat recovered from Mr. Davidson's operation, had to be scrapped, owing to her very weak condition, so she was to go home for a few weeks to recuperate, and to return to the hospital and his ward on October 1st. Janie smiled inside, for the date was her fortieth birthday. She searched his face, for she needed information concerning the operation. "Tell me, Mr. Baines, what do you intend to do, what type of operation is it?" The doctor hesitated, then he realised that this young woman was firm and sensible and placid in her outlook, moreover she had a right to know, it was her body. "I have to amputate the breasts, those growths are quite ghastly." He hesitated, then, "I have to do all I can to prolong your life and to help you to recover."

Then suddenly, as Janie stared at her doctor, and tried to take in all that he was saying, another doctor's features over-shadowed his. Of course, she thought, Dr. Reynolds, the spirit doctor – didn't he say that at any time he would be with them to help them if they needed it? She could write to the medium, Mrs. Northage, and ask for her help in contacting him. Mr. Baines looked at her rather anxiously. "You do understand what I am telling you?" he asked, "It's the only way that I can help you to prolong your life."

Janie stirred, "And how much longer, will it prolong my life?" she asked.

"Perhaps six months, maybe a bit longer, and I will help you all I can."

"You mean with the pain? Oh yes, I am sure you will help me there."

"Then you will come back on that date? Rest all you can, and try not to worry."

"No, Mr. Baines, I will not promise to come back, I must do something first; but I do promise that I will not neglect it."

The doctor glanced sharply at her. "Well, I don't know what you mean, but I do think you will be sensible."

*   *   *

As soon as Janie returned home, she told her husband all that Mr. Baines had said concerning her condition, and immediately he made a phone call to Mrs. Northage who had been very concerned over Janie's serious illness. She promised to talk with Dr. Reynolds and phone them back. The result was that the next evening the phone call was made, and a sitting had been arranged in six weeks time for Janie and John to have a talk with the doctor and to see what could be arranged. In the meantime, he would constantly visit Janie to give healing to restore her strength.

The day of the sitting arrived and Janie and John set off for Newstead Abbey, Nottingham, where Mrs. Northage had lately moved. Her secretary, Mr. Stocks, had sent the new address; the name of the property was 'Pinewoods,' and as neither of them knew the locality at all, John decided to arrive there before dark.

Dusk was falling as they found the Mansfield Road; John drove along slowly as they saw that the houses lay well back from the road, with most of the fronts wooded with trees. They were looking for the name 'Pinewoods', but it was very difficult for them to see the house-names at all in the fast-fading light. Janie was very anxious as she glanced at her watch and saw the time was five forty, and the sitting was due to start at six o'clock, and once it had commenced the door could not be opened to let them in. Suddenly, they came to a recess in the road and John turned into it. He got out of the car to investigate and saw some high gates further on and the name 'Newstead Abbey' in large letters across the top. He peered inside and saw a drive leading away in the darkness with thick shrubs and trees on either side, but no sign of a house.

He came back to the car, puzzled and rather angry, "I can't understand all this, what's the matter with us that we can't find a house called 'Pinewoods'? There's Newstead Abbey and that's on the address, but it must mean just the locality."

Suddenly, he saw some lights glow through the darkness to the left of the Abbey gates; "There must be a house in there," he exclaimed, "I'll go and see if they can help us." Soon he was back, disappointment in his face; "No – they've just moved in and they're strangers to the district." He looked at his watch. "I don't believe it," he stormed, "it's turned six o'clock." He stared helplessly round and across the road into the darkness. "There's some sort of large building over there with light in some of the windows. I'll run over and see if somebody can help me." Jane could not answer, she felt sick with despair.

As John moved away from the car, he heard one of the abbey gates open and the dim figure of a man emerged, and came up to them. "Are you Mr. and Mrs. Bailey," he enquired, "from Birmingham?" He went on as they both replied. "I'm sorry you've had a job finding us – I didn't realise that you don't know this district: The sitting had started, then the doctor came through to tell us of your predicament and that you were just outside the main gates. He asked me to put on a light and come out to fetch you: By the way, I am Mr. Stocks, Mrs. North-age's secretary."

Janie was elated with wonder and thankfulness, so, Spirit did know when you needed help. John looked bewildered as he turned to help his wife out of the car; "You mean there are houses inside those grounds? No wonder we couldn't find 'Pinewoods'.

"Stay in the car, Mrs. Bailey," Mr. Stocks interrupted. "we'll drive to the house, it isn't far. Yes, Mr. Bailey, there are several houses scattered about the grounds, but most of them are hidden by the thick foliage."

They turned down the first side path, passed a couple of houses, one either side, and turned in at the drive of a bungalow. There was no outside light, but a strong light from the window of the bungalow reflected on to the path of the front garden, showing in the background many pine trees from which the bungalow derived its name. Mr. Stocks showed John where to park the car, then asked them if they would like any refreshment before they went into the Sanctuary; both thanked him, but explained that they had stopped for tea on the journey, and they did not wish to keep the doctor waiting any longer.

Instead of going towards the house, Mr. Stocks led them to a wooden shed standing solitary at the side of the path leading to the front door of the bungalow. He pushed open a door and ushered them inside to a fairly large room, dimly lit by a red light. Mrs. Northage sat with five other people in as a circle, and she extended a warm welcome to the couple. She also apologised for the difficulty they had experienced in finding 'Pinewoods'. There were three vacant chairs within the circle and Mr. Stocks indicated where he wished them to sit, while placing himself in the other one. Janie noticed a small table at his side on which stood two small table-lamps, one of which supplied the red light; while near to his right hand lay a large writing pad, with pencils near at hand. There were also several glasses of water.

Mr. Stocks glanced round the circle. "Right, everybody comfortable? We'll make a start and get the doctor back again."

The red light was extinguished and immediately the trumpet, which stood in front of the medium, rose gracefully up into the air and glided around the whole of the room, then came to each sitter and lightly tapped each one on the shoulder. A young girl's voice spoke, the sound coming from just above the heads of the sitters.

"Good evening, my friends, it's nice to see you with us once again. This is Ellen speaking." The trumpet moved over to Janie and John and hovered over their heads. "I wonder if you remember me, Mr. and Mrs. Bailey? I know you have been here only once before, that was last year; I am Ellen Dawes and I am helper to Doctor Reynolds."

"I could not possibly forget you, we had such a marvellous time. Whatever the reason for us being here, we are thrilled to meet you again." And Janie's voice broke with the emotion she felt, while her husband murmured his appreciation. The trumpet went back to the centre of the circle, while Ellen told them doctor would be with them in a moment.

The trumpet rose again in the air, then came to rest just above John and Janie. "Good evening, Mr. and Mrs. Bailey. I am glad you got safely here; I am sorry Mr. Stocks did not send you precise instructions as to where

Mrs. Northage lived. There are very few people outside of Nottingham who realise that there are houses inside the abbey grounds. I am glad I received your thought that you needed help, Mrs. Bailey, or you might have been going back to Birmingham now with nothing achieved."

A shiver ran down Janie's back as she recalled the anxiety of the last half an hour. "I didn't know you would pick up my thoughts, doctor, but how glad I am that you did."

"Yes, my dear, I told you the first time we met that I would be able to receive your thoughts when you needed help for yourself or others. Now, I want to know how you are, and if you are gaining strength after your operation."

"Yes, I do feel better, and my appetite is improving, thank you, doctor," Janie replied. "But I have been rather worried about Mr. Baines' report of my condition; I don't feel like having that operation. What do you advise, doctor?"

"You do understand what Mr. Baines was saying to you. You do realise he is hoping to prolong your life some few weeks?"

Doctor Reynolds' voice sounded urgent; Janie guessed it was important for her to know that her health was in a very grave condition. "Yes, doctor, I do realise that, that is why we got in touch with you. We are desperately hoping you can help me in some way." Janie's voice broke, she could say no more.

"Yes, my dear, I will help you all I can: We have had many discussions on our side about you, and the powers that be have decided that I should operate when you are a little stronger. In the meantime I will come to you at night-time to freeze the growths, so that they will not grow any more. When you are in pain send a thought to me and I will come and put you to sleep, and when you awaken, the pain will be gone. Try to get in as much rest as possible to reserve your strength. Now, put all this to the back of your mind and enjoy the rest of the sitting. I will be back before it is all over."

So saying, the doctor moved away to have a word with the other sitters and his medium. After a while, Ellen came through again to tll Janie that her mother wished to speak to her, but that her voice might not be clear as she was upset and weeping because of her daughter's illness. Janie thanked her and told her she would do her best to console her mother.

Ellen left; then the trumpet rose in the air and glided over to Janie. It caressed her shoulders and head before gently settling on her lap, while, out of the air just above her head, a voice broken with tears, spoke.

"Oh, my little girl, what have they been doing to you? You had such a bad time in hospital and Doctor Reynolds was with you quite a lot; when he did have to leave you he always left a lovely young nun to watch over you. I know that you saw her several times; and when your breathing stopped and you left your body I was with you while Doctor Reynolds helped the hospital doctors to get your heart going again. You did not want to go back, you cried awfully, you wanted to stay with me; I had to remind you of John and the children. Young

Angela would have broken her heart, had you not returned home. In any case, you have important work to do in the future, so I am told. So you see, you are going to get well. But, I must go now, there are so many waiting to speak. Give my love to Frank and your sisters. I will come again when you are here." The voice faded, but Janie felt a soft kiss on her cheek, and somehow, she felt comforted.

She felt bewildered and a little confused. How matter-of-fact Doctor Reynolds sounded, as if it was the usual thing for spirit doctors to operate on earth people. To her, it was the most wonderful thing in the world. How he would do it and what the procedure would be, she had no idea, she only knew she could never go back to the hospital again. Mr. Baines was a kind and understanding doctor, and she knew he would do all he could to prolong her life; but at the outside, he could only give her a few months. Also, her mother had said that she – Janie – had important work to do in the future. Another mystery, what important work? But Janie felt she could wait for that to materialise, as it seemed that Doctor Reynolds and others in the Spirit World had planned a future for her on the earth plane.

Doctor Reynolds came back as he said he would do at the end of the sitting. He reassured Janie that he would visit her every night to see how she progressed, and when he deemed her ready for the operation, Doctor Isa (Mrs. Northage) would send for her. He wished them a good journey home and said he would send someone with them to guide them through the darkness of the strange roads. John and Janie thanked him profusely and after some refreshment, started for home after one of the strangest journeys they had ever made.

Then one day they received news that proved very upsetting. Mrs. Northage had been taken ill with meningitis of the spine and it would be many weeks before she was able to work with the doctor. But he would still look after Janie and freeze the growths to keep them from growing any larger. He would also be with her at times when she was in pain and had sent her thoughts out to him.

CHAPTER 26:

AN AMAZING OPERATION.

Unfortunately, the circle had been postponed during Janie's illness as the rest of the sitters were not keen to sit without Janie and John's support. But Janie knew their prayers were for her and she derived a great deal of strength from them.

October the first, when she should have returned to the hospital, came and went, and Janie wondered about Mr. Baines, and his thoughts of her. She wondered, if perhaps she should have got in touch with him, to tell him of her plans, but the thought of his disbelief and the fact she was waiting for a dead surgeon to operate, appalled her, so she decided to let matters rest.

The winter came and slowly dragged by, and many times she had to send out her thoughts to the spirit doctor for his help, and each time she was gently put to sleep and pain and discomfort had left her when she awakened.

She knew her husband worried about her, and sometimes she felt anxious herself. Also, her eldest brother stormed up one evening to see them, and to let them know in no uncertain way that he considered them both mad, and he called John a murderer. Janie was very angry. She told him that the decision to go the spirit doctor was her own and she could do what she liked with her own body. She had got all the faith in the world that the cancers would be removed at the right time, and had she kept her appointment at the hospital, she had the premonition that she would never had left the operating table. Her brother left them abruptly, banging the door behind him. They had no more contact with him for many years, and Janie often wondered what he thought of her return to health and strength and yet he was never man enough to see them and to hear the whole story. He seemed very bitter against Spiritualism and she thought it might be because Fank, his younger brother, of whom he was very fond, had taken to it. It was a pity things had turned out like this, as she loved both her brothers.

From time to time John phoned the family of Mrs. Northage to enquire how she was and he was told that the medium was progressing slowly. The breakdown in her health had been brought on by overwork, for apart from seances, she held a healing clinic each day and saw as many as two hundred patients. She was a wonderful healer and bone manipulator and worked under the advice and instruction of Doctor Reynolds. He said he could not rush her recovery as the main treatment she needed was complete rest. Until she had fully recovered, he could not use her for his work as the ectoplasm he used from her body would not be in the right condition.

Then, at last, towards the end of June, Mrs. Northage herself phoned up to tell them that Doctor would like to operate on Saturday, July 15th, and asked her to be there at seven o'clock in the evening.

John started straight away to make plans for the journey, as Frank had expressed a wish to go and if possible, be present at the operation. Also, they would need extra petrol and as that commodity was still on ration and needed coupons, Frank always seemed to know someone whose 'car was laid up' and who were not using their monthly coupons.

Steve Fisher had arranged to borrow his bosses' large car, for in addition to the extra passengers, Steve thought it would be more comfortable for Janie. Then about ten days before the appointment, Janie was making her way upstairs, very slowly, as she did everything those days, when she felt herself swaying backwards and in the effort to save herself from falling, she hit her feet against the front of the stair and slithered down several of them. A sharp pain rent her inwardly, as she lay where she was, afraid to move. After a while, feeling better, she struggled to her feet and made her way to the settee. She said nothing to John when he came in from work; she felt there was no need to unduly worry him. Later, she discovered she had haemorrhaged quite badly, and still she said nothing to her husband.

Later that evening the phone rang and John went into he hall to answer it, coming back looking white and very grave. "That was Mrs. Northage," he said staring hard at his wife. "She said when you fell down the stairs today, you burst a growth in the intestine; Doctor heard your call for help and he has stopped the bleeding. He said you are to rest as much as possible between now and Saturday, when he wishes to operate. He dare not leave it any longer. Why didn't you tell me you had fallen like that? It's a good thing that Doctor heard you. Perhaps, it's just as well the operation has been brought forward a week. I must get on to Steve and Frank about the car and petrol." So saying he rushed out of the room towards the phone, without waiting for his wife's explanation.

Janie sighed with relief. She was feeling very weak and tired, but there was a warm thrill inside her at the thought of the spirit doctor watching over her and knowing about her accident. John finished his phoning and came back slowly into the room, a puzzled frown on his face.

"It looks as though the changed date is going to cause a bit of trouble," he said, "Steve said that his boss will need his car this coming Saturday. He's going away for few days. And Frank says he'll never get the petrol coupons in time for Saturday. There's another friend he can try, he'll let us know how he gets on. He said you are not to worry, we'll get you to 'Pinewoods' somehow." But inside Janie was not worrying; she had complete trust in the doctor, she knew something would be arranged.

Friday night arrived and the arrangements had to be finalised. Steve had to take his own car instead of his bosses' larger one and fortunately, he had sufficient petrol for the return journey. To Frank's great disappointment and also his sister's, as she would have welcomed her brother's presence, there was not room in the car for him. It was only a small car, and Steve's wife and niece sat in the back with Janie, while John sat beside the driver.

After an uneventful journey they arrived at 'Pinewoods', and were met and welcomed by Mr. Stocks, who showed them into the lounge. He explained that Mrs. Northage had already gone into the Healing Sanctuary, with her daughter, Mrs. Difford, and Mrs. Stenson, both trained nurses, to prepare for the operation. He said he would bring in tea and making his excuses, disappeared towards the kitchen.

After tea, Mr. Stocks disappeared again and Janie, wondering where he had gone, felt herself growing excited and wished she knew a little more of what was likely to happen and the procedure. She was not afraid, but just a bit bewildered by the unknown.

Mr. Stocks returned, to tell them things were almost ready in the Sanctuary. He showed the two men to the bathroom and advised them to wash their hands thoroughly as the doctor might call on them to help. After this he led them to the Sanctuary.

It was quite dim inside, just a small bulb, switched on and hanging from the ceiling. Mrs. Northage sat in a high-backed wooden chair, to all intents and purposes fast asleep, and well away from the medical couch at the other side of the room. Two nurses greeted the little party, then Mrs. Difford went to the medium and drew two very thin black curtains across the front of her, which turned the space where she was sitting into a cabinet. This was to allow total darkness for the spirit doctor to materialize. Coming over to Janie, she led her to the couch, after telling the others to sit quietly, until the doctor arrived. Janie was undressed and a loose gown placed on her, after which the nurses helped her on to the couch and covered her legs with a light blanket. The light was then switched off and the nurses began the hymn "Nearer my God to Thee," in which they all joined.

After a short prayer given by Mrs. Difford, the red light was switched on and Doctor Reynolds stood before them. After greeting them, he turned to John and Steve to explain that the operation would normally take about two hours, but because of Mrs. Northage's health, he must work very fast and complete it in less time. Would they be willing to help him? The two men willingly gave their assurances that they would do all that the doctor wished them to do.

Mrs. Stenson came forward with two white medical coats which both of them put on, then moved over to where the doctor was pointing, the opposite side of the couch to where he himself would be working. Doctor then turned his attention to the patient and asked her how she was, "I feel wonderful, Doctor, and very excited – and oh, thank you for doing all this for me, I just don't know what to say." Gazing up into that kind gentle face, with the lovely deep brown eyes,

Janie felt the tears start to her own. Doctor gave her a penetrating gaze, then smiling gently, he quietly said, "The future will unfold, my dear, and you will have much to say, but now we must get on."

TESTIMONY OF JOHN HANDS, HUSBAND OF THE AUTHOR OF THIS BOOK.

I, John Hands, am writing this account of the operation on my wife by Dr. Reynolds. I and Mr. Steve Fisher were asked to help, as Mrs. Northage had been ill and the doctor did not wish her to be too long in trance. We had to wear white coats and theatre masks, and I stood at the operating table with a nurse and Mr. Fisher.

Within a few minutes of Mrs. Northage going into trance (she was sitting in a cabinet at the end of the Sanctuary) Dr. Reynolds appeared at the opposite side of the table. After greeting us all and talking for a few moments, he asked my wife if she wished to remain awake or go to sleep, but in either case she would feel completely normal. My wife replied she would like to remain awake to see what happened. Doctor then proceeded to swab the parts to be operated on with disinfectant; he then set more swabs about the places and passed his hands across the affected areas. The patient's breasts were opened, and the abdomen treated likewise. Doctor Reynolds then took a bright green pencil torch from the trolley and shone the light into the cavities, showing three cancers lying deeply inside.

Doctor then explained that the cancer in the intestines had burst and with swabs he removed the pieces, carefully placing each in a receptacle. He cleaned the site with swabs, each of which as it came from the wound was covered in blood and pus. There was a strange sound as each cancer was drawn from the breasts, and after this all wounds were carefully cleaned. The doctor not only removed the cancers, but also the hairlike roots which, he said, would prevent the growths from re-forming. They were over most of her chest and abdomen, and while working in the region of her left armpit a haemorrhage started which caused the doctor some concern, and he said he would have to fetch something from the Spirit World to stop it. He disappeared through the floor, but in a few moments reappeared with a crystal-like bottle containing a colourless liquid with which he soaked a swab and pressed it under my wife's armpit, telling her to close her arm tightly against it.

On being satisfied the wounds were clean, he gradually closed them up sideways, until what appeared to be scratches were left. Then he placed his hand sideways on each wound and drew it across from end to end, and as his hand passed over the edges of the wounds they were sealed completely, not even a scratch remaining. Finding the haemorrhage had stopped, he sealed up that wound likewise.

During the time that I was passing swabs to the doctor, he worked so fast that he occasionally grabbed my fingers instead of the swab. When the operation was over he said he would go, while a Dr. West came to examine his work, and, stepping back about two feet from the table, he sank through the floor, and within two minutes Dr. West appeared in his place, the latter being of different height and build to Dr. Reynolds. He said very little as he went over the patient's body with a torch, taking particular notice of the place where the bleeding had occurred. Then he told my wife that she had very little to worry about, providing she carried out Dr. Reynolds' instructions, which he would later give to her. He then remarked that the doctor had made a very good job of a very difficult case, and wishing us all good night, he left.

When Dr. Reynolds reappeared, he gave instructions that all the swabs must be carefully collected and the surgery thoroughly scrubbed down with disinfectant, as the cancers were of a particularly contagious type. Also, when we had examined them in the electric light, they must be burned, and not taken away, as when they were kept in a spirit solution, the patient never really got well. He then told my wife that the freezing he had done would last until the next day, but then she would be in a fair amount of pain; he would, however, be there to help her. This took place as he said, my wife being very ill for a few days, but within a week she was up and has progressed very well since.

The operation took one hour and twenty minutes. When it was over we went outside, and Mr. Fisher remarked that though he had witnessed everything that had taken place, he just could not believe his eyes.

That is just how I feel about it.

(It has been thought advisable to leave this text as it first appeared in A PATH PREPARED by Alan MacDonald, rather than use the fictional names used elsewhere in the book.)

CHAPTER 27:

A WONDERFUL GIFT.

Janie gradually regained her strength and resumed her normal life, but often her thoughts would stray back to that wonderful evening, as she lay on the couch gazing into the doctor's face as he operated. He talked to her quite naturally as he worked; his was no ghostly figure, but that of a normal human being, dressed in a surgeon's white coat and hood. She had to think deeply to realise he was not of this world, but was indeed an angel. Now, she thanked God for the illness, for it was a means of bringing her face to face with the true meaning of the manifestations of Spirit.

Many times in the future they received invitations to visit 'Pinewoods', as Doctor Reynolds wished to keep in touch with his patient until she was quite fit and well. At one of the sittings, Janie received a lovely surprise. A young nun materialised in front of her and she recognised her "watcher" of the hospital. She took Janie's hands in her own and pressed them gently, speaking softly in a foreign tongue, while making the sign of the cross. At this point, Ellen Dawes broke in to advise the nun that her speech could not be understood and she must speak in English. She apologised, and still holding Janie's hands she continued talking, giving her name as Cynthia.

She confirmed that she had sat at Janie's bedside in the hospital to watch over her and to report her progress to Doctor Reynolds. Janie's excitement knew no bounds as she surveyed the lovely figure – tall and slim, dressed in a wonderful gown of some amazing white material, something between a delicate satin and silk. From the neck line to the waist was embroidery of fine lace insertions and coloured needlework of shaded lavenders and pink. Over the head was worn the nun's conventional head-dress of the same material. The whole effect was slightly luminous, while a faint pleasing perfume pervaded the air.

Then after a few moments, Cynthia announced that she must go to fetch something, which she wished Janie to have, but that she would not be long away, and sinking swiftly through the floor, she disappeared. Janie tried to get interested in the rest of the seance, but her mind was in a whirl, watching every moment for the nun's return. Then suddenly she was there, and taking her hand as before, pressed into it something that seemed to be warm metal; glancing down, Janie saw a crucifix, such as nuns wear, but its condition was dull and slightly mildewed, as though it had been long in damp conditions.

"My dear," explained the nun, "I wish you to have this as a present from me; it is the crucifix I wore during my time on earth. Many times it has comforted me and given me strength and courage when I was ill and in pain. You see, my dear, I also suffered from cancer, and I am afraid I obtained no relief from the pain of it. You will see on the back, the imprints of my finger nails, which I pressed into the crucifix when the pain was bad." And so saying, Cynthia gently turned over the cross and pointed to two indentures on the upright stem. Janie, puzzled, stared at the marks, then up at the nun's face: "But, Cynthia," she asked, "where have you been, to fetch this?"

"Oh, my dear, of course, I did not realise that you are not acquainted with apport procedures. Presents that your loved ones wish you to have, are sometimes brought by 'helpers' and come into the seance room through the roof. Then the trumpet floats upward to receive them and take them to the recipient, but I was given permission and help to fetch my own gift, which was buried with me, in my coffin. It was the only thing I ever had that belonged to me and now I wish you to have it and to know the comfort it can give. God bless you, my dear, and I will always be with you when you need me."

Janie glanced up through her tears to murmur her thanks, but the lovely soul had already gone. The voice of Dr. Reynolds was heard, advising Janie to soak the cross in neat antiseptic for forty eight hours to get rid of the coffin emanations, and to wash her hands after the seance. He also advised her to wrap it in a handcherchief until she got home.

And so ended one of the most spectacular seances, as several other people received lovely apports and many materialisations were seen. Also, the whole of the time spirit voices were heard. The seance lasted just over three hours.

CHAPTER 28:

"A SNIP, A TWIST AND A STITCH."

The years rolled by, and Janie was kept busy helping her husband with his electrical business. Young John had gained a place at Fircroft College and then on to Keele University. Angela had grown into a very attractive teenager and worked in the cashier's department at the Austin motor works.

About this time, six years after Janie's spiritual operation, she began to experience great pains in her lower abdomen. The least jolt or push would cause her enormous agony, so she phoned Mrs. Northage for help. She told her that Doctor had told her that he suspected something was wrong with Janie, and he had better have a talk with her. The next weekend the medium was coming to Birmingham to stay with friends, so she arranged to meet Janie and John at the home of mutual friends on the Saturday evening.

On that occasion the doctor did not materialise, but spoke in the direct voice. He told Janie that her pelvis had collapsed, the bladder was badly displaced, while the tubes leading to the kidneys were in a bad tangle. She must go back to the General Hospital as soon as possible and insist on seeing Mr. Samuel Davidson, the surgeon who had operated on her in 1949. John asked the doctor if there was a reason why his wife should see that particular surgeon. "Yes," came the reply. "It is very easy for me to send my thoughts to that gentleman, and in the case of an emergency, very useful. Of course, he is not aware that he is responding to my thoughts; he thinks he has a sudden idea; but no matter, so long as he carries the idea out and the patient benefits. I will give you a sample of what I mean. I will be with you when Mr. Davidson gives you the initial examination, and before you leave him, I will impress on him to say, "Do not worry, Mrs. Bailey, we will soon have you well again; a snip, a twist, and a stitch, and it will all be over."

"Thank you, Doctor, I will remember that, but..." she hesitated, not quite knowing how to explain her own doubts concerning herself. "I don't mind going into hospital, I'm only worried about the holdup in our circle, as we have just got going again after a long break. Will it take long before I am able to sit again."

"But, my dear," the doctor replied, "there is no need for you to worry, you are already developed and a fully fledged medium. You are like a building, fully wired and equipped for electricity, but still waiting for the power to be switched on. Your sitters will supply the power you need. I think at the moment you need more sitters, but remember, you must experiment until perfect harmony is reached. If you are uneasy over any of the sitters, that they are not suitable, you must ask them to leave and you must replace them. You must go on like this, until at last you feel at ease and happy with your sitters; then you will have good results. But always aim for the highest; it will take longer for your sitters to attain, but it will be well worth it in the end. Your phenomena will produce spiritual manifestations, which will be very wonderful for you. Now, I think, with Doctor Isa's permission, we will try a little experiment, just to show you that you are a medium."

So saying, the voice was directed to Mrs. Northage's direction and a whispered consultation took place. The voice gathered normal strength and was directed at Janie again. "Mrs. Bailey, we are going to use the power that Doctor Isa always uses, but it will be drawn through you and your mediumship will be used and you and your friends will see the results. Doctor Isa will not take part in any way with this experiment. Just sit easily and naturally."

In a short while, Janie felt a gentle pull in the region of her solar plexus and throat, and suddenly the three trumpets standing on the floor in front of her, rose gracefully into the air and floated around the room. Then they came to rest in front of and just above the sitters, and three voices were heard greeting them. They gave their names and the information that they were pilots of the Spitfire aeroplanes that belonged to Air Chief Marshall Downing's squadron. They were friends, and had been killed at about the same time. Then they formed the three trumpets in the shape of an aeroplane, and sent them flying with great speed round the room, while they accompanied them with the necessary sound effects.

After this wonderful display of power the three visitors bade the sitters 'goodnight' and other loved ones and friends took their places. The sitting went on for about an hour, the doctor then explaining that he must call it to a close because of Janie's poor state of health. Afterwards, there was great excitement among the friends as they discussed the circle and how they could get new sitters to increase the power; but they all realised that nothing could be done until Janie was well again.

In two or three days, Janie received her appointment from the hospital and duly presented herself to Mr. Samuel Davidson. He confirmed Dr. Reynolds' diagnosis, and explained that it was caused during her operation in 1949. Apparently, the stitching to the internal wound had taken place just when the patient's breathing stopped, so measures had to be taken to restart it again, and the stitching could not be completed, as the patient's condition was very grave.

"I am sorry about it, my dear," the surgeon said, "but I will do all I can to make matters right. I must have you in hospital right away, nurse will give you the appointment." He wished her "good morning", then turned away to wash his hands. The nurse helped Janie off the couch and steered her to the door which she opened. "Go and get dressed, my dear," she said, "then wait for your appointment."

"Yes, thank you, nurse," Janie replied, but her eyes gazed wistfully in the direction of the doctor, who was washing his hands at the wash-basin. Then suddenly she remembered her handbag lying on the floor against the leg of the couch. "Oh, nurse I've left my handbag, I must get it. I won't be a moment." She walked as slowly as she dared across the room. Then suddenly Mr. David-son turned and walked towards the couch. He looked sharply at his patient and noticed her apparent apprehension.

"Oh, Mrs. Bailey. I thought you had gone. Now don't be worried, you will be quite all right. A snip and a twist and a stitch and it will all be over."

A smile broke out over Janie's face, she almost threw her arms around the doctor's neck. Instead she blurted out:

"Oh, Mr. Davidson, I was waiting for you to say that, thank you so much," and leaving the astonished man, she stepped happily over to the door.

So Janie spent another month in hospital: there were complications both with the operation and the treatment afterwards, but Janie was not worried for she knew that Dr. Reynolds would not leave her until she was well on the road to recovery.

CHAPTER 29:

THE SPIRIT WORLD NURSERY.

It was sometime before Janie felt able to sit in her circle again, but sadly by then the numbers were depleted and she felt there would have to be more sitters to build up the power needed. So, they carried on hoping for the best, when suddenly Mr. Steve Fisher passed to the higher life, leaving his wife and niece broken-hearted. The circle was held at their home, so once again, it was postponed till happier times.

Two years passed, and both John and Angela, son and daughter of Janie, were married and settled in their homes. Then one day, nearly five years afterwards, Angela confided to her mother that she and her husband were disappointed that a baby had not been sent to them to complete their happiness.

She had talked it over with her doctor and he had arranged for her to see the leading gynecologist of the West Midlands. In the following months she went into hospital twice for examination under anaesthetic, but the result was negative. It was impossible for her to have children. Janie's heart ached for the young couple and she gave the matter much thought. Then suddenly, one evening, the face of Doctor Reynolds flashed into her mind; the kindly friendly face with the soft brown eyes. He had done so much for her, and spent so much time with her, could she possibly impinge on his good nature again, to help her daughter to happiness?

She thought the matter over for several days, then with a sudden urge she flew to the telephone and rang Mrs. Northage at Newstead Abbey. After a long talk, Mrs. Northage promised to tell Dr. Reynolds all the facts and ask his opinion. Then she added that she did not think she had ever had such a request before. She would get in touch with Janie when she had the verdict.

So Janie sent up her prayers while she waited; she could not settle to anything as she longed for the phone to ring. Then at last the doctor's message came. He had been to examine Angela as she slept, and at the present time it was impossible for her to have children; but he would obtain help from the Spirit World to see what he could do. In the meantime, he advised Jane that she should not tell her daughter about his intervention, in case of disappointment if he were not successful.

More than a year afterwards, Janie woke one night to find herself standing at the side of her bed. All the signs present told her that she had left her body, and glancing down she perceived that to all intents and purposes, she was fast asleep. She wondered if she was on her usual healing mission or if this was something special, then suddenly a hand sought hers and the well-loved voice of her guardian angel told her that she (or he), had something to show her.

As was the custom on those occasions Janie closed her eyes and clung to her companion as the two rose up into the air and floated swiftly towards their destination. It was a thrilling sensation and Janie had grown to love it. In a moment or two she felt the warm sun on her face and she opened her eyes. They had landed o a well kept lawn with lovely flower beds surrounding it. The fragrance from the flowers was wonderful and very pleasing to the senses.

Near at hand was a path, down which the two walked; turning a bend at the bottom a magnificent sight met their eyes. In front of them stood a wonderful white circular building. Whatever it was built of, Janie had no idea, but the whole effect was a beautiful lace design, while shooting out from the domed roof were delicate shafts of different hues. Above the building and right across it hung a golden rainbow with different coloured lights directed into the roof. Janie stood still in breathless admiration; a feeling of love emanated all around her bringing tears to her eyes, while a feeling of great humility filled her being.

Her companion took her hand and led her to the building, up some steps and into a spacious hall. The white lace effect was present in the circular walls, while here and there pictures of babies and little toddlers adorned the walls. From the ceiling, subdued coloured rays spread around the space above them; the whole effect magnificent, yet restful and soothing. Janie's guide led her to one of the many doors leading off the hall and as it silently opened the two went inside.

Janie glanced around in amazement; the floor space was covered with lines of babies' cots, while several white-robed attendants appeared to be looking after them. She was led to the third cot of one line, and glancing down at a lovely cuddly baby lying there; somehow, the little face was familiar. "Oh," she exclaimed, "what a lovely baby; who is it?" And the voice of her guide replied. "That is the son of Angela and Robert; you will see his name over the cot above your head."

Janie looked up and saw in glowing lights, like a glittering diamond, the name "Sean Robert." She had seen the first name in writing before, but had no idea how to pronounce it. She turned to her companion, "May I tell Angela and Robert that I have seen him, and please – when will he be born?"

"When his mother's body is ready to receive him, but only Dr. Reynolds know when that will be. Yes, you may tell his parents that you have seen him and that you know his name. They will tell you how to pronounce it. Now sit for a few moments to dwell on this night's events, so that you will remember every detail when you awaken in your body." And as Janie sat down she remembered why the baby's face was familiar; he was so like his mother when she was a baby.

She did as she was bidden; then as the two turned away to leave the nursery, Janie questioned her guide. "Have all these babies to be born on the earth plane?"

"Yes," came the answer, "When the mother's body is ready to receive them – at the right time and the right place. Everything is planned and organised. The date of your little grandson's birthday is already known; I do not know it, its only known to those who have charge of these things."

Janie woke as usual in her body, and she lay a long while thinking of the night's events. The wonder of all the fascinating things she had seen, and the rows of cots with the precious burdens waiting to commence their destiny on the earth plane. A wave of sadness swept over her at the thought of those souls leaving the happy lands of the Spirit World to sojourn for a while in the Earth World, to gain material and physical experience.

As soon as possible, she was on the phone to her daughter to tell her the happy news. Angela was beside herself with joy. From past experience, she knew she could rely on her mother's information. When she was told the name, she said, "Hold on, Mom, while I get Rob, he'll tell you about the name, I don't know." Janie repeated her news, but her son-in-law was silent and she thought he had gone away. But surprise had robbed him of his speech. Then he said, slowly, "Mom, you are a witch! I don't understand how you got your information, but I do know that that is the name I've chosen, if we have a son. You see, Angela and I have agreed that if we have a child, Angela will choose a name for a girl, and I will do likewise for a boy. I would like to call him 'John', but we have so many Johns in the family, and 'Sean' is Celtic for 'John'. So, when can we expect the little chap, Mom?"

"I do not know; when Angela is ready for him, I believe, it's all in the capable hands of Dr. Reynolds. So, we must be patient and wait."

* * *

About this time, Janie began having trouble with her legs, and her doctor advised her to leave the hills and find a bungalow on the level ground somewhere. Her husband was very reluctant to leave 'Melita', but he realised the very large garden was getting too much for him, and the large house too much for his wife to look after. So, after many 'viewings' and disappointments, they found just what they wanted in Kings Heath, near to where they used to live before the war. When they made the appointment to see this bungalow, another couple were there who seemed very enthusiastic with everything, which made Janie feel very apprehensive; but she consoled herself with the thought that if they were meant to live there, things would go their way.

After the agent had been in conversation with the other people in another room, they left, and he turned his attention to Janie and John. He told them that he thought the other people would have it, but they would let him know the next morning. Nervously Janie also said that she would like it and the agent replied that if she could make him a better offer, she should ring him early next morning. On the way home, John said that they would not be able to make much of an offer, as apart from the money they would have by selling 'Melita', they had no funds, (Jane and John had bought the house on Mrs. Cornforth's death.) Janie realised that the sale of the one almost covered the purchase of the other.

But her heart was set on the bungalow, she felt they were meant to live there; so silently she sent a petition to the spirit friends for help.

That night she awakened to find herself walking in one of the lovely gardens of the spirit world; she had been there many times before, so she looked around for a familiar face, and saw her brother Frank coming towards her. She ran to meet him and after greetings, he told her that he had received her thoughts and he could help her if only she would do as he advised. He told her to ring the agent in the morning, and to make an offer of an extra fifty pounds. It would be accepted. Janie looked at him in astonishment. "But that doesn't seem enough to entice him, I thought we should offer at least two hundred pounds, but we haven't got that much."

"Then do as I say, and things will be alright. You are meant to live there. You'll have a lot of work to do, to bring the place up to your liking, but we will see that you receive the strength to do it."

In the morning, Janie told her husband of her encounter with her brother. For a few moments he stared silently at her, then, "And what are you going to do about it?"

Janie hesitated, she felt she was losing her enthusiasm. "Well, I think we should ring the solicitor; we can but see what he will say."

"Well, I think he'll think you're raving mad; still, I'm off to work. I'll leave you to it."

Janie's heart sank at her husband's attitude, and long after he had gone, she sat thinking of Frank. She remembered the urgency in his voice and the earnestness in his eyes; he never did waste words. If he believed in what he told her, why should she doubt it? It would not hurt to give it a try.

She got up quickly and went to the phone, glancing at the number as she dialled it, then waited breathlessly. A man answered, and she asked him if he were the solicitor for the property she was interested in. He said he was, so taking a deep breath, she made her offer. For quite a while there was no reply, and Janie wondered if he had passed out. Then a quiet voice repeated her offer and asked if she meant it?

"Yes," replied Janie, "Of course I do."

"Right; I'll get in touch with the owners and ring you back in half an hour."

Janie thanked him and put down the phone. For half an hour she did not move, just sat and prayed.

When at last the phone rang she jumped with alarm, and had to force herself to her feet. She murmured a faint "Hello" into the phone and heard the solicitor's voice reply: "Mrs. Bailey, I don't understand it, but you've got your bungalow. Mrs. Arnold has accepted your offer. Now, perhaps, you'll tell me what this is all about, I know you've got a story."

So Janie told him about the conversation she had had with her dead brother the night before, only she told him it was a dream, as he might not understand about people leaving their body and jaunting off to meet their loved ones who 'had gone before'.

"Well, I've never heard anything like it, but it has certainly paid off. I hope you will be very happy in your bungalow."

All excited. Janie rang her daughter to give her the news. Angela was very pleased for her mother and told her she would do all in her power to help with the moving. She in turn had some news for her mother – she felt changes in her figure and had experienced morning sickness; her doctor had made an appointment with the maternity hospital to see the gynaecologist.

Janie was overwhelmed with joy and told her daughter she would go with her at the end of the week. The outcome of it all was that Angela was well advanced in pregnancy and the doctor most bewildered by it all.

The miracle baby ws born on February llth, 1968, a beautiful, perfect little baby. His mother had told everyone she was expecting a son and when questioned said that she had great faith in her mother's dreams, as she called them, and she had known for some time that she and Robert would have a son named Sean Robert. When Janie went to the hospital to visit her daughter, she was allowed to enter the nursery with a nurse and to pick out the little one for herself. There she found him, laying in his cot just as he had been in the spirit world.

CHAPTER 30:

THE PARTING OF THE WAYS.

Young Sean was a few months old when at last his grandparents were able to move into their bungalow. They found it strange at first, for they both missed the larger garden and the surrounding hills; but after a while, when they had experienced the advantages of their new home they were both glad they had made the change.

One night, after they had retired for the night, Janie woke up to find herself walking in the "Garden of Memory", in the Spirit World, so called because it was near to the earth boundary,and was the first place that earth people met their loved ones who dwelt in the Spirit World. They usually spent the time together talking of the old times they had when all were on the earth plane. Memories came flooding back, hence the name 'Garden of Memory.'

But on this occasion, Janie saw her mother coming quickly across the grass to meet her, a worried expression on her face. She embraced her daughter, then earnestly gazed into her eyes. "Janie, you must go back, that electrical contraption on your bed is still switched on and the bed is getting very hot. John is still in his body and fast asleep, also your body is there, of course."

Janie brushed away her mother's alarm. "No, Mother, I always switch it off as soon as I get in bed. I'm sure it isn't on now." Looking up, she saw her brother Frank coming speedily over to them, she ran to meet him. "Janie you must go back immediately or you will regret it. You can come back, we will wait for you."

"But Frank, I can't think what this is all about. I know I put my hand under the pillow to switch off the electric blanket, like I always do."

"But Janie, you were late getting to bed tonight, and John wanted to go to sleep, so he switched off the blanket. You switched it on again."

Janie gave her brother a long look, then alarm spread over her face and turning, she was gone like the wind.

Reaching the bedroom, she quickly entered her body, and immediately felt the heat. She switched off the blanket and throwing back the bedclothes, she frantically shook her husband and tried to tip him out of bed. But her efforts were in vain, so she went on shaking and yelling at the top of her voice. John opened his eyes and stared in bewilderment at his shouting wife; then the heat got to him, and swiftly he tumbled out of bed.

Luckily, the bed did not burst into flames, but two hours later, over a cup of tea, Janie told her husband the story.

*   *   *

About this time, John began to feel unwell, but Janie could not persuade him to see his doctor. It worried her to watch him making the effort to work in his beloved garden and greenhouse, for it seemed that his strength was slowly leaving him; she sent up a prayer for help.

One morning, he woke up with a severe cold, and without consulting him, she rang for the doctor. When he arrived, before she took into the bedroom, she told him of her anxiety for her husband over the last few weeks. When the doctor came out his face was grave and he told her that her husband should see a consultant as he thought he needed an operation. But John flatly refused, he hated the thought of going into hospital, and his wife thought it was because of his experience as a young man when he spent three gruelling months in hospital and nearly lost his leg. She tried to tell him that things were different now, and that great strides forward had been made in surgery, but he would not listen.

One evening at the end of February, they both sat watching television: There was a comedy on which amused Janie and she turned to see if her husband was enjoying it as she was. To her great consternation and amazement, she saw a narrow band of white mist surrounding his head, face and body. She turned quickly away, but dread filled her heart, for she had seen that phenomenon before – it meant that John was near to the end of his earth life.

Her thoughts raced here and there – was there anything she could do to help him? She knew he would not listen to her, but he might listen to John, their son who lived near to his work in Welwyn Garden City; but she could not phone him while his father was in the house, she would have to wait until the morning when her husband would be in the garden, so that would mean phoning the college where her son worked.

Accordingly, the next morning when she was alone in the house, she contacted her son, who promised to visit them at the weekend which was only a day away. She went out into the greenhouse to tell her husband of their son's forthcoming visit.

The outcome of the talk between father and son was that a visit to the consultant was promised, for as young John pointed out, surgery might not be necessary. Perhaps some other treatment could be given.

In due course, John received the appointment from the hospital but before he could keep it, Janie awoke one morning to find her husband unconscious; he was rushed to hospital but died the next day, on March 12th 1971, just two weeks after Janie had seen the strange phenomenon around the outline of his body.

Sometime after John had left the earth-plane, Janie awoke one night to find herself walking in a beautiful park; there were plenty of people about, a mixture of earth folk and their spirit friends, but they all seemed to be going in the same direction. She gazed around to see if any of her friends were there, and to her great joy she spied her husband coming across the lawn to meet her.

After greeting her, he guided her footsteps to walk with the crowd, explaining that he had a lovely surprise for her. Leaving the park, they all entered a most delightful garden and taking a main path approached a most magnificent white building. It was circular in shape, with massive pillars supporting a high domed roof, while between each pillar masses of glorious flowers grew in orderly profusion, the colours blending in delightful patterns that were a joy to behold. As Janie drank in all this wondrous beauty, a lump rose to her throat, while tears grew in her eyes; she wanted to ask questions, but she could not speak.

They walked with the crowd to the entrance of the building, up a flight of wide shallow steps and into the foyer. Flowers were everywhere, blending harmoniously with coloured lights, while the delicate fragrance of the flowers filled the air – the whole effect was soothing and pleasing.

Several archways led to different parts of the building, and the people seemed to know which on they should go through.

John chose one and led his wife through it, to emerge into a vast amphitheatre, whose arena was covered with musical instruments of all kinds, some known to the earth visitor, but the majority she had never seen before. She was filled with amazement as she saw the people filling the many tiered seats and she suddenly found her tongue.

"Oh, John, are we going to attend a concert? What a wonderful place! Are you sure they won't mind me staying? I do hope I will remember all this to tell them all when I get back."

John laughed as he drew her forward towards the seats. "Yes, we are attending a concert; so, they won't mind you being here. You have been invited along with other earth folk. I'll do my best to help you remember. Now come along, there are many of your old friends waiting to greet you before the concert starts." And so there were, loved ones, friends and neighbours, some whom she had known when she was a little girl.

At last the musicians entered the arena and the concert commenced. Janie sat enraptured, her hands clasped loosely over her husband's knee, never had she heard such exquisite melodies and such perfect playing. If only she could remember some of it when she went back to the earth-plane.

At last, it was over, and the musicians left the arena amid the joyous clapping of the crowd. John helped his wife to her feet, saying she must hurry now, as she had been there for three hours. Janie could not believe it and wished she could stay there for ever; but her husband pressed her arm and smiled wryly at her, "It is not time for you yet, you have work to do, but time will pass."

He walked with her to the borders of the earth-plane and kissed her farewell. Janie closed her eyes and wished herself home, then she opened them again and found she was lying in her bed. She glanced at the clock and noted it was four o'clock. She lay thinking of all she had seen and heard, and desperately she tried to hum some of the lovely tunes she had heard. But though she knew they were still in her mind, she could not bring them to her voice box. Perhaps it was not for her to do so. If some of that music was meant to come to earth real musicians would be chosen as channels, as they had been in the past. Janie only knew she had been greatly priviledged to spend that wonderful three hours in heaven.

*   *   *

For some time after her husband's death, Janie was uncertain what to do with her life, but do something she must. She thought again of the little Spiritualist Church opened by Jim Arnold all those years ago, how he and the members of his circle had worked hard to turn a decaying scout hut into a fit habitation for the power of Spirit. All had gone well until the outbreak of war had separated the friends and sent them scattering in different directions. Janie knew the church had been taken over by other workers and had flourished all those years.

Now, through the devotion and perseverance of a band of those early workers a fine new church had been built in Springfield Road, Kings Heath, not far from where she now lived. She made up her mind – she would go to that church and make friends, and if they needed help she would offer her services.

So, Janie, thinking back over the years, marvelled at the way she had been directed and guided. Her whole life had been linked to Spirit and the manifestations that had been granted to her. For what purpose? Why had she been chosen? Perhaps, God knew that she would bear witness to the glimpses of truth that would be given to her: He needs teachers, but these teachers must have experience and be willing to share those experiences in all humility and love.

Janie placed her feet firmly on the path that she knew she must take and there was a great sense of purpose and peace in her heart.

THE END